IMPROVING
THE HUMAN CONDITION

THE STORY OF SANFORD HEALTH

IMPROVING
THE HUMAN CONDITION

THE STORY OF SANFORD HEALTH

JEFFREY L. RODENGEN

—— FOREWORD BY ——
DENNY SANFORD

—— INTRODUCTION BY ——
KELBY KRABBENHOFT

Edited by Elizabeth Fernandez and Loren Moss
Design and layout by Sandy Cruz

Write Stuff Enterprises, LLC.
1001 South Andrews Avenue
Fort Lauderdale, FL 33316
1-800-900-Book (1-800-900-2665)
(954) 462-6657
www.writestuffbooks.com

The publisher has made every effort to identify and locate the source of the photographs included in this edition of *Improving the Human Condition: The Story of Sanford Health*. Grateful acknowledgment is made to those who have kindly granted permission for the use of their materials in this edition. If there are instances where proper credit was not given, the publisher will gladly make any necessary corrections in subsequent printings.

Publisher's Cataloging-In-Publication Data
(Prepared by The Donohue Group, Inc.)

Rodengen, Jeffrey L.
 Improving the human condition : the story of Sanford Health / Jeffrey L. Rodengen ; edited by Elizabeth Fernandez and Loren Moss ; design and layout by Sandy Cruz ; [foreword by Denny Sanford ; introduction by Kelby Krabbenhoft].

 p. : ill., plans ; cm.

 Includes index.
 ISBN: 978-1-932022-59-9

 1. Sanford Health—History. 2. Multihospital systems—United States—History. 3. Integrated delivery of health care—History. I. Fernandez, Elizabeth. II. Moss, Loren. III. Cruz, Sandy. IV. Sanford, Denny. V. Krabbenhoft, Kelby. VI. Title.

RA981.A2 R64 2013
362.11/0973   2013930940

Also by Jeffrey L. Rodengen

The Legend of Chris-Craft

The Legend of Dr Pepper/Seven-Up

The Legend of Honeywell

The Legend of Briggs & Stratton

The Legend of Stanley:
150 Years of The Stanley Works

The Legend of Goodyear:
The First 100 Years

The Legend of Cessna

The Spirit of AMD

The History of American Standard

The Legend of Mercury Marine

The Legend of Pfizer

The Legend of Gulfstream

The Ship in the Balloon:
The Story of Boston Scientific and the
Development of Less-Invasive Medicine

NRA: An American Legend

The Legend of Discount Tire Co.
WITH RICHARD F. HUBBARD

The Legend of Polaris
WITH RICHARD F. HUBBARD

The Legend of La-Z-Boy
WITH RICHARD F. HUBBARD

Jefferson-Pilot Financial:
A Century of Excellence
WITH RICHARD F. HUBBARD

The Legend of Werner Enterprises
WITH RICHARD F. HUBBARD

The Legend of Sovereign Bancorp
WITH RICHARD F. HUBBARD

The Legend of
Universal Forest Products

Changing the World:
Polytechnic University—
The First 150 Years

In it for the Long Haul:
The Story of CRST

Office Depot: Taking Care of
Business—The First 20 Years

A Passion for Service:
The Story of ARAMARK

The Legend of Con-way:
A History of Service, Reliability,
Innovation, and Growth

Commanding the Waterways:
The Story of Sea Ray

Past, Present & Futures:
Chicago Mercantile Exchange

The Legend of Brink's

Kiewit: An Uncommon Company:
Celebrating the First 125 Years

The History of Embraer

A Symphony of Soloists:
The Story of Wakefern and ShopRite

JELD-WEN: Celebrating 50 Years

Innovation, Passion, Success:
The EMC Story

Old Dominion Freight Line:
Helping the World Keep Promises

Moretrench

For a complete list, visit writestuffbooks.com

Completely produced in the United States of America

10 9 8 7 6 5 4 3 2 1

TABLE OF CONTENTS

FOREWORD
BY DENNY SANFORD

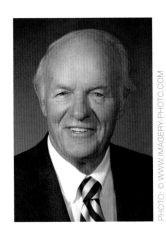

I HAVE A SAYING TAPED TO THE WALL IN MY OFFICE: "ASPIRE TO INSPIRE BEFORE you expire." Those are, for me, words to live by, so it's been a privilege to play a role in Sanford Health's inspiring story, helping ensure that excellent health care and groundbreaking medical research make a positive difference in the lives of people all over the world, both now and in the future.

My personal story begins in a tiny home on the east side of St. Paul, Minnesota, where my mother, Edith Sanford, succumbed to breast cancer when I was four years old. At the time, I didn't know what cancer was, just that my mother went away and never came back. As I grew up, however, I began to understand that with early detection, my mother's life might have been saved. What a difference better health care could have made.

My father, older brother, and I carried on, and by my 16TH birthday, my brother and I were helping out in our father's clothing distribution company. I learned from that experience how to anticipate people's needs, present opportunities, close a deal, and keep commitments.

After high school, I enrolled at the University of Minnesota, where I majored in psychology. That was, for me, great training for a career in business and, ultimately, philanthropy. Following my graduation, I joined Armstrong Cork Company and quickly became one of their top salesmen of flooring materials. After signing the largest client in the company's history, I asked my boss for a $50 a month raise, which would have brought my monthly compensation to $475. When he said no, I quit and promised myself that one day, I would be my own boss, and I would always treat my employees well. Before long, I became a manufacturer's representative, launching a nationwide construction-materials distribution company called Contech and eventually starting a manufacturing company called Sonneborn Building Products. We made and distributed architectural chemical materials for several of the nation's largest construction projects of the period, including the World Trade Center. I took the company public in 1972 and sold it at a considerable gain in 1982, making my shareholders very happy.

With funds to invest and a desire to help other entrepreneurs, I then went into the venture capital business, organizing some 28 different projects and bringing 18 to the public marketplace. One day, a dear friend in the Young Presidents Organization called. He urgently wanted to meet. "You are buying my bank in South Dakota today," he told me. "I'll give you a really good deal. You have to buy it." That day, I bought First PREMIER Bank in Sioux Falls, South Dakota. South Dakota just happens to be the credit card capital of America, so I recruited the best minds in the industry, Miles Beacom and Dana Dykhouse, and we launched the very successful PREMIER Bankcard. That was a great investment.

In Sioux Falls, I found a community of honest, hard-working people who are committed to making a positive difference in their families and communities. I bought a residence there and proudly began to call South Dakota home. When I started getting to know my neighbors and community leaders, I was particularly impressed by the team at what was then Sioux Valley Hospitals and Health System, now Sanford Health. Kelby Krabbenhoft, a born leader and true visionary, and his key executives, Dave Link, Becky Nelson, and Brian Mortenson, provide a great set of services to every community they're in while always looking for new communities to serve and better ways to make a difference. They're conceptual. They're forward-thinking. They're highly respected. They are, in short, second to none.

So when Kelby told me they wanted to build a new hospital for children that would raise the standard of care for little ones throughout the region, I wanted to be a part of that. I was passionate about the project, the plans, the team, and the cause, and I'm very proud to have assisted in the creation of the symbolic but very real and breathtaking achievement that is the Sanford Children's Hospital, the Castle of Care.

A few years later, Kelby and his team came to me with a plan to transform the course of health care in our region and beyond. Their initiative would advance all the programs already in place and add some exciting new components as well, including a project to cure type 1 diabetes in my lifetime, a plan to build clinics in underserved communities all over the world, and a commitment to finding other cures through patient-oriented research.

I said yes to Kelby's plan, partly because I believe in him and his organization, partly because I'm grateful for an opportunity to give back to South Dakota after all it and my PREMIER family have given to me, and partly because this is the kind of life-saving, game-changing opportunity that excites me the most. On the day that Sioux Valley Hospital announced it was changing its name to Sanford Health, I walked on clouds, buoyed by gratitude for the chance to help make a difference in the lives of millions of people by supporting Sanford Health's bold initiatives to improve the human condition.

What follows is a story of absolute magic. Read how researchers at the Sanford Project for type 1 diabetes are getting closer to the cure every day. Learn how children in this country and in places as diverse as Africa, Europe, and Mexico, children most vulnerable to disease and malnutrition, are being given proper health care, which brings hope for the future to them, their families, and their communities. See what the Edith Sanford Breast Cancer initiative is doing to stem the tide of more than 200,000 new cases of breast cancer in America each year, partly by creating a national biobank of DNA samples that will be made available to researchers and clinician scientists throughout the world, accelerating the path to a cure. Know that the people at Sanford Health are dedicated to work that is compassionate, cutting edge, and transformative. The people at the Sanford Health organization have consistently exceeded their own goals and promises! This is their remarkable story. I hope it inspires you as much as it does me.

INTRODUCTION

BY KELBY KRABBENHOFT
CEO OF SANFORD HEALTH

I REMEMBER THE FIRST DAY. I REMEMBER PUTTING ON THE SUIT, DRIVING to work, and parking the car. It was winter, December 1996, when I was met by Sioux Valley Hospital's legendary leader, Lyle Schroeder, who had tremendous pride in the institution. I would soon marvel that he could say "SiouxValleyHospitalSiouxFallsSouthDakota," as if a single word with a single syllable. Lyle was an icon of Sioux Valley Hospital, a remarkable man who had been CEO at Sioux Valley for 36 years.

I was grateful to inherit an organization that had earned such a wonderful reputation and was performing well across the board. My first and most important duty was to not drop this "precious egg" I had been handed. Even Paul Bunyan didn't leave shoes like these to fill.

Sioux Valley had already begun the careful transformation into an integrated health care system, and a very sincere and dedicated board of trustees had been looking forward to completing the transition and growing the organization once I arrived. You see, size is important in medicine. You've got to have it to provide the highest standard of care, and you've got to have it to attract the best and brightest, and to provide them with the greatest professional opportunity. Before we could contemplate significant expansion, we would first create a model patient delivery system that integrated physician, hospital, and health plan services.

As we grew, we knew we had to build and enhance an already strong culture. We have to maintain what I call "four tight corners"—operational excellence; strong relationships with our physicians and staff; a strong community presence; and beyond all else, taking great care of the sick, injured, and infirm.

In the pages that follow, you will learn how the generosity of Denny Sanford provided an extraordinary transformational gift that has expanded our vision, accelerated our growth, and extended the horizons of our potential. It is important to note that the scale of gifts that Denny Sanford has shared with us far exceeds, in modern dollars, those of the Mayo brothers, Johns Hopkins, or even the lasting legacy of the Carnegie library endowments. The most recent of his gifts is $100 million for the establishment of the Edith Sanford Breast Cancer initiative, named in honor of his mother. With Denny's philanthropy to Sanford Health exceeding $600 million today, his visionary generosity will continue to touch the lives of countless children and families for all generations to come.

We have a long journey ahead of us. Sometimes it's hard to contemplate that only six years have passed since we received The Gift from Denny Sanford, a magnificent $400 million contribution that ignited the Sanford Initiatives with a focus on finding cures, serving globally, and changing the landscape of our communities with new health care resources. It's just been three years since the great merger of MeritCare and Sanford Health, when I also received a leadership baton from retiring, legendary MeritCare CEO Dr. Roger Gilbertson. And, it's only mere months since our mergers with North Country Health Services and Medcenter One, and we have joined with many more physicians and community institutions in just a few years.

Sanford Health now includes a dedicated team of 25,000 employees and 1,200 physicians who provide care across 120 communities in 36 hospitals; 225 clinics; 39 long-term facilities, home care, hospice programs, and wellness centers. Together with a network of children's and primary clinic locations across the country and the world, Sanford Health brings health care home for more than 2 million people. We have only recently broken ground on the new Sanford Fargo Medical Center and we have much, much more to accomplish.

With size, however, comes increased responsibility. We ponder the potential of Sanford Health as defined by our principal market as between the Mississippi River and the Rocky Mountains. Today, that translates into a daunting 220,000 square miles of commitment. Our goal is to provide access to care within 45 minutes of anywhere within that vast region.

Looking ahead, hopefully a long time from now, I will be sitting in a rocking chair on the porch of my cabin at Lake Hanska, Minnesota, and reflecting upon my time with Sanford Health. I will ask myself, "What more could I have done? Did we achieve best-in-class outcomes in our five centers of excellence: heart, cancer, children's, women's, and orthopedics/sports medicine? Did we discover a cure for type 1 diabetes? Did we make a difference?" I feel assured because I know that together we are making a difference and changing the course of things, and I am proud to be part of it.

We're truly on a mission at Sanford Health. We want every physician, every nurse, every employee to feel it, to say, "I want to come to work every day and make a difference."

ACKNOWLEDGMENTS

RESEARCHING, PREPARING, AND PUBLISHING *Improving the Human Condition: The Story of Sanford Health* could not have happened without the help of many individuals.

Sharon Peters and Sandy Smith assisted with the principal archival research. Their thorough and careful work made it possible to publish a great deal of new and fascinating information about the origin and evolution of Sanford Health. Executive Editor Elizabeth Fernandez and Senior Editor Loren Moss managed the editorial content, and Senior Vice President/Creative Services Manager Sandy Cruz brought the story to life. Gratitude is extended to Brian Mortenson, president of the Sanford Health Foundation, for providing early direction and continued support that helped shape the direction of the book. The author thanks Jane Heilmann, Sanford Health senior strategist of corporate communications, for her historical perspective, expert review, and critical services provided throughout the development of the book. Thanks is due to Andy Wentzy, director of the Sanford Initiatives, for providing valuable input and information for the story.

Thanks is extended to the many individuals who were interviewed and were generous with their time and insights, including James W. Abbott; Pamela Anderson; Terry Baloun; Miles Beacom; Mike Begeman; David Beito; Daniel Blue, MD; Dean Bresciani; Evan Burkett; Victor L. Campbell; Mikal Claar; North Dakota Governor Jack Dalrymple; David Danielson; South Dakota Governor Dennis Daugaard; Dana Dykhouse; Jim Entenman; Barbara M. Everist; Tom Everist; Michael Farritor, MD; Jerome D. Feder; Rick Giesel; Roger L. Gilbertson, MD; Mark Glissendorf; Paul Hanson; Richard D. Hardie, MD; H. Eugene Hoyme, MD; Thomas C. Hruby; Garry Jacobson; John Jambois; South Dakota US Senator Tim Johnson; Dan Kirby; Dave Knudson; Kelby K. Krabbenhoft; Ruth Krystopolski; David Link; Bill Marlette; Barry Martin; Dennis Millirons; Lauris Molbert; Ronald M. Moquist; Cindy Morrison; Brian Mortenson; Don Morton; Becky Nelson; Andy North; Charles "Pat" O'Brien, MD; Rob Oliver; Michael Olson, MD; Mark Paulson, MD; Bruce G. Pitts, MD; Alex Rabinovitch, MD;

Paul F. Richard; former South Dakota Governor Mike Rounds; Bill Sanford; Chuck Sanford; Denny Sanford; Lyle E. Schroeder; Barbara J. Stork; Brent Teiken; David Thomas, MD; South Dakota US Senator John Thune; Larry Toll; and Ed Weiland.

Gratitude is also due to the members of the Sanford Health Story Committee for sharing their knowledge and experience and ensuring completeness of the story. Members include: Arlys Nelson; Jacquie Kluck; Stacy Jones; Kelli Koepsell; LaNeil Bartell; Brian Mortenson; Paul F. Richard; Bruce G. Pitts, MD; Dave Knudson; Jane Heilmann; Andy Wentzy; and John Paulson.

Finally, a special word of thanks is extended to the current and former staff and associates at Write Stuff Enterprises, LLC: Christian Ramirez and David A. Tumarkin, senior editors; Danielle Taylor and Cristofer Valle, graphic designers; Lynn Jones and Nicole Sirdoreus, proofreaders; Lisa Barclay, Patti Dolbow, Barbara Martin, and Erika Wallace, transcriptionists; Donna M. Drialo, indexer; Amy Major, executive assistant to Jeffrey Rodengen; Marianne Roberts, president, publisher, and chief financial officer; and Stanislava Alexandrova, marketing manager.

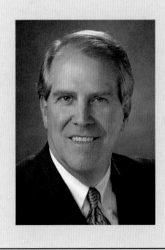

The author extends special thanks to John Paulson, Sanford Health vice president of corporate administration. Paulson has been with Sanford Health for more than 25 years, and his vast knowledge of the health care field proved instrumental in ensuring accuracy. His constant guidance and dedication have made this book possible and all of us at Write Stuff are sincerely grateful for his assistance.

CHAPTER ONE

THE MEETING OF THE MINDS

You have two leaders, both of whom are driven and both of whom are in it for the right reasons, and that's an awesome combination.

—Mike Rounds
Former governor of South Dakota[1]

A SINGLE MOMENT IN THE AUTUMN OF 2005 WOULD SET A COURSE that would impact the lives of millions—first in South Dakota, but soon enough, across the entire globe. Two talented, big-thinking men sat across from each other. Kelby Krabbenhoft had made a passionate and eloquent plea, outlining an ambitious plan to Denny Sanford, entrepreneur and philanthropist, for transforming the delivery of health care and curing disease. The time had come for Denny to ask a fundamental question.

"How much?" Denny asked. "What would it really take to accomplish these things?"[2]

He was intrigued by the proposals made by Krabbenhoft, CEO of Sioux Valley Hospitals and Health System, a well-respected health system headquartered in Sioux Falls, South Dakota. Denny was a resident, and it was in South Dakota where he had found success in the banking and finance industry.

Krabbenhoft estimated implementing the plan would cost $400 million. Krabbenhoft and the two executives sitting beside him, Becky Nelson, then president of Sioux Valley USD Medical Center, and Brian Mortenson, president of the health system foundation, anxiously awaited Denny's reaction.

Much was riding on Denny's response. A profoundly generous man, Denny had previously donated $16 million to help build a state-of-the-art children's hospital for the health system, evidence that he had a great deal of faith in Sioux Valley Health System,

Above: Denny Sanford, philanthropist and business leader, was determined to use his fortune to help improve the lives of people across the globe.

Opposite: The Sanford Children's Hospital in Sioux Falls, South Dakota, was made possible due to Denny's generous $16 million donation.

Right: From left to right: Kelby
Krabbenhoft, Dave Link, Brian
Mortenson, and Denny. Along
with Becky Nelson, they
helped coordinate the largest
charitable donation ever made
to a health care organization.

and in the CEO's ability to utilize his donations in greatly improving the health of
patients across the region.

A History of Giving

Krabbenhoft, Nelson, and Mortenson had flown from Sioux Falls to Denny's vacation
home in Vail, Colorado, that September morning of 2005 to present the request.
Krabbenhoft remained confident his proposal would be carefully considered. He had
developed a close relationship with Denny over the previous two years and knew
Denny had an appreciation for solid business strategies and groundbreaking initiatives.
During his nine years in Sioux Falls, Krabbenhoft had already achieved a track record
of success, having profitably grown Sioux Valley Hospitals and Health System, begun
construction of new facilities, increased the number of physicians integrated with the
system, and launched a group health insurance plan.

These initiatives were only the first steps in a far-reaching plan to elevate Sioux Valley
Hospitals and Health System into bold and new territory, initiating a vision that would
contribute to improving health and health care not only for the people of Sioux Falls
and the Upper Midwest, but also for people around the country and perhaps the world.
He wanted to place his health system on the national stage with an eye toward ultimately
altering the way health care is regarded, approached, and dispensed.

Krabbenhoft believed that because of the challenges and uncertainties of reimburse-
ment provided for health services throughout the industry, and the need to constantly

Below: Becky Nelson,
president of Sioux Valley USD
Medical Center at the time,
participated in the Vail,
Colorado, meeting that led to
Denny's $400 million donation.

Making an Impact

Denny Sanford committed the extraordinary sum of $400 million because of his faith in the Sioux Valley Hospitals and Health System and his faith in CEO Kelby Krabbenhoft. He explained, "Kelby is absolutely a great visionary, and he sees things that none of the rest of us sees. And he can sell those ideas."

Not only did Denny feel an instant connection to Krabbenhoft's ideas, he was certain Krabbenhoft could generate the enthusiasm that would position the organization perfectly for the future.

According to Denny, Krabbenhoft was "supported by a great staff of people. He has surrounded himself with the best and brightest, and that's what makes great organizations great. It's not how good you are; it's how good your staff is."[1]

Before he made the $400 million request, Krabbenhoft had introduced Denny to top health system executives who could present their operational strategies and objectives, and Denny had been quickly impressed with the depth of leadership, singling out David Link, Becky Nelson, and Brian Mortenson for special praise.

According to Denny:

[Krabbenhoft has] the best team going, and it's capable of continuing to grow and expand. ... The different types of things that I do are all project oriented. I love Sioux Falls, I love South Dakota and so forth—and Fargo and all the rest.

When Kelby laid this initial consideration out to me, it was essentially project oriented, building children's clinics, and finding a disease, one specific disease, that we could really have an impact on in my lifetime.[2]

Above: Former South Dakota Senate Majority Leader Dave Knudson has served on the Sioux Valley board and is now senior vice president and strategic advisor for Sanford Health.

upgrade and expand programs and services, philanthropy could provide the assistance needed to create dynamic opportunities for innovative breakthroughs in medical research.[3] Krabbenhoft's dedication first helped to forge the friendship between the two men. In the fall of 2003, attorney Dave Knudson, a mutual friend who also served as Denny's legal counsel, suggested to Krabbenhoft that the timing might be right to seek Denny's support to build a new children's hospital in Sioux Falls. According to Knudson, Denny always had a soft spot for kids.[4]

Krabbenhoft wasted no time. He flew to meet with Denny in Arizona on December 13, 2003.

"If you give us $16 million, I'll go raise $16 million in 18 months, and we'll get this thing under way," Krabbenhoft said as they sat in the conference room at the airport.

To the best of Krabbenhoft's knowledge, no one had ever raised $16 million in Sioux Falls, but he was sure he could do it,[5] and he wanted to assure Denny that he and his team were eager to work together as equal partners in funding the venture.[6] The two men spoke earnestly of the prospect of transforming pediatric care in Sioux Falls and beyond.

"That's a good project you have there. Let me think about it," Denny replied.[7]

The two shook hands, and as Krabbenhoft walked off to fly home, Denny called him back. "Let's do this. It's a good idea."[8]

Below: During their meeting in Vail, Colorado, Krabbenhoft proposed renaming Sioux Valley Hospitals and Health System. He asked Denny for permission to use the name Sanford to recognize the transformational effect of the gift and to honor Denny. It would also personalize the system's identity with great character and charitable spirit.

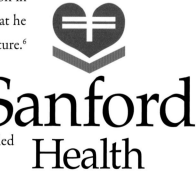

The appreciation each man had for the other had grown in the months between Denny's initial $16 million donation and the September 12, 2005, meeting in Vail. Health system and foundation officials had been diligent about keeping Denny informed of progress on the children's hospital that would bear his name as well as about general Sioux Valley Hospitals and Health System updates, often in face-to-face meetings.

A Bold Request

In 2005, Krabbenhoft prepared an ambitious plan to "ask Denny to transform the [Sioux Valley Health] system," as he explained to Senior Executive Vice President Dave Link.

"What are you going to ask him for?" Link asked.

Krabbenhoft, CEO of Sanford Health, helped transform the health care system with programs to serve across the region and around the world.

The Impact of The Gift

Kelby Krabbenhoft sensed a kindred spirit in Denny Sanford, an entrepreneur who was imaginative, forward-thinking, and impatient for ideas to blossom into action. He trusted Denny. "The relationship between Denny and I was founded on … what's down in here about 8 inches inside our gut, close to our spine," he said. "That's the way we think."[1] A commitment to donate $400 million requires an extraordinary man like Denny, and an extraordinary team to bring a challenging vision to reality.

Krabbenhoft knew he could speak frankly and expect the same in return. He knew Denny would both understand and appreciate the potential impact of his gift as few people could, and once Denny shook hands on a deal, there would be no hand-wringing or second-guessing after his word was given.

Krabbenhoft knew that launching a relationship of this magnitude with any donor implied a certain amount of ongoing engagement. "Denny would relish the chance to start a journey of that kind," Krabbenhoft recalled.[2]

As Krabbenhoft explained when he announced what would be characterized as The Gift, "They say there are certain opportunities that come once in a hundred lifetimes. This is the moment. Our intent is to change things."[3]

The impact would be profound, even transformational, just as Krabbenhoft promised. He noted:

Denny Sanford's gift drives our ability to be a leading medical research organization with comprehensive infrastructure, to advance excellence in medical education programs, and to be recognized for premier pediatric patient care and research. [And with his generosity,] he has transformed us and our vision for leadership in the 21ˢᵗ century— "To Improve the Human Condition."[4]

"Four hundred million dollars," Krabbenhoft replied. "I want us to do research," Krabbenhoft told Link. "Denny is smart. He's got a chemical background. He gets it. I want to do research, and I want to find a cure. The next thing I want is a world-class campus and medical enterprise here in Sioux Falls. I want to do that right."[9]

"Let me think on this," Link replied.

After some consideration, Link approached Krabbenhoft with another proposal. "I think we should build children's clinics in several locations around the country," Link said.

Krabbenhoft agreed that it was an idea with the possibility of improving the lives of others. He recognized that making a request of such magnitude would be a bold, unprecedented move, yet he remained certain Denny possessed both the vision to understand the importance of his proposal, and a generous philanthropic spirit.

Mortenson requested a meeting with Denny as soon as possible, and it was arranged to be at his vacation home in Colorado. Denny had said, "You know, Brian, you really don't have to come all the way out here. I'll be back in Sioux Falls later on this month and we can find the time to get together then."

However, Mortenson knew that this particular meeting was too important to wait. According to Mortenson:

I knew Kelby wanted to do some real special things and have a dedicated time apart from distraction and in a setting that would be conducive to this. I said, "You know, we

Denny has remained passionate in helping children. He donated $16 million to help build a new children's hospital known as "The Castle of Care" in Sioux Falls. That endeavor marked the start of a lasting relationship between Denny and Sanford Health.

would really like to make this meeting a little bit special and we have a lot of things to share with you and really are interested in kind of a 'miniretreat' if you will. We truly would love to come and visit with you there if that's all right with you."

Denny replied, "Oh, okay. That's fine."

He could tell there was an agenda with a little bit more substance.[10]

Krabbenhoft, Nelson, and Mortenson flew out to meet Denny in Vail, Colorado. After lunch, the four of them returned to Denny's home and fell into a comfortable conversation discussing the progress at Sioux Valley. Krabbenhoft began to describe a shining opportunity for significant impact and growth as a health system, expounding about his vision to forever change the health care landscape, not just locally, but far beyond.

He wasn't interested in merely building new facilities, he explained. He wanted new buildings, but they must be superbly equipped, and they must house extraordinary people and programs. Krabbenhoft imagined a newly redesigned campus featuring the latest in medical technology and fully equipped to embark on challenging new research projects. He also proposed launching a wide-ranging network of pediatric clinics as well as collaborative efforts with what would become the Sanford School of Medicine at the University of South Dakota. Krabbenhoft used the analogy of The Manhattan Project as a dramatic example of the progress that can be achieved when the world's top scientists devote attention to solving a single challenge. "What would happen if we were to devote that kind of focused attention, energy and resource, and intellect to the discovery of a cure for a major disease?" he asked.[11]

The Sanford Health campus now holds sculptures honoring Denny's magnificent charitable spirit and love of children, including a sculpture with his grandchildren, which stands in front of the Sanford Children's Hospital.

Denny and Krabbenhoft have worked tirelessly to improve health care access for millions of people worldwide and combined their visionary leadership and philanthropy to chart a course for "Improving the Human Condition."

Krabbenhoft proposed launching a massively funded project that would lead to curing a devastating disease in a relatively short time. He explained to Denny, "I'm not going to mess around. We've got to find a cure. That's what you can do that will transform our organization to be one that goes after a cure, not after a journal article, not after a notation. We're not going to improve science. We're going to solve the disease."[12]

This groundbreaking effort would be known as "The Sanford Project."

"It was an amazing, exhilarating conversation," Mortenson recalled. "Becky and I jumped in when we could get a word in edgewise," Mortenson recalled. "But that wasn't often."[13]

Krabbenhoft and Denny grew increasingly excited as they discussed the possibilities, but there was just one more matter to consider.

"We are not only asking for your consideration of this megagift to get these things done, but we'd also like to ask you for your name," Krabbenhoft said.[14]

The $400 Million Question

After outlining their proposal, and making his appeal for a record-breaking $400 million donation, Krabbenhoft and his team sat in silence. The possibilities Krabbenhoft had envisioned all hinged on Denny's support and generosity.

Denny leveled a direct gaze at Krabbenhoft before replying. "Let's get it done," he said.

That meeting marked the first step toward a profound transformation of the health care field, both regionally and across the globe.

Later, when reminded by Krabbenhoft about the request to use the Sanford name for the health system, Denny's response was "I don't need my name on anything more—but if you insist, I guess I should be glad my name isn't Krabbenhoft."

CHAPTER TWO

DENNY SANFORD

He's definitely "Denny" as opposed to Mr. Sanford. He's a very common-folks kind of person, a very informal type of person ... and very approachable, and enjoys meeting and talking with people. ... He has a good grasp of what's important and what's not, and has that ability to concentrate on the important issues.

—Dave Knudson
Denny Sanford's attorney and current
Sanford Health strategic advisor [1]

Above: William B. Sanford, owner of a small clothing distribution company, holds his second son, Denny, at just a few weeks old.

Opposite: One of the forms of relaxation the ever-in-motion Denny Sanford has always enjoyed is a quiet sail on churning waters.

BORN ON DECEMBER 23, 1935, TO A WORKING-CLASS COUPLE ON THE POORER side of Saint Paul, Minnesota, Thomas Denny Sanford—he dropped the Thomas as soon as he had a say about such things and was known as Denny thereafter[2]— was a precocious child faced with adult-sized challenges.

A whip-smart kid though a half-hearted student, Denny lost his mother to breast cancer before he reached his 5TH birthday.[3] He grew up in a modest apartment with his brother Byron, who was four years older, and his father[4] during the post-Depression era when children learned at a very young age the importance of hard work. From the age of eight, as soon as he was big enough to lift boxes and fold garments, he helped out in his father's work-clothes distribution business.

In his youth, he loved challenge and adventure, constantly moving and seeing things through to fruition. In these formative years he learned the Upper Midwest values of industriousness, respect for self and others, and self-sufficiency. By age 16, he was hitting the road every weekend and during summers with his older brother, peddling their father's wares. "He was always very conscious of finances. ... He had a box in his bedroom where he kept change ... all neatly stacked in there," recalled younger brother Chuck Sanford, born when Denny was 11, after his widower father Bill remarried.[5]

Denny was small and baby-faced, so when he was young, he took to wearing a man's hat to add gravitas.[6] He discovered an affinity for sales work because it gave him a chance to get out and meet people, "and see what the other part of the world was all about," he recalled decades later.[7] Even then, he began to recognize in himself an inherent tendency to rethink conventional ways of doing and approaching things.

His drive for constant momentum and his need to challenge the status quo made him a natural leader in his pack during his teenage years. It also once got him into a legal scrape that would change his life. The summer following high school graduation, he was arrested for a street fight and was sentenced to 90 days in a juvenile facility. The judge paroled him after 36 days when he agreed to enroll in the University of Minnesota.[8]

He joined the Chi Psi fraternity, made a halfhearted stab at being a student, and bought an MG with money he had earned and saved.

Denny's first-choice major of premed fell apart after only a couple of semesters

While still in college at the University of Minnesota, where he was in a fraternity and was a barely average student, Denny buys his first car, an MG.

at the University of Minnesota. "I got a couple of Ds and my advisor said, 'What else would you like to do?'" Denny recalled.[9] He settled on psychology, and finished up a semester late—"a C minus grade but I got the job done"[10]— in December 1958 with a degree and an offer from Armstrong Cork Co. to become a sales and marketing manager. The company provided 12 months of training, which he completed at the top of his class.[11] He excelled

1935

DECEMBER 23
Thomas Denny Sanford is born in Saint Paul, Minnesota, the second of two sons. After his mother dies when Denny is 4, his father eventually marries again; that marriage yields Denny a younger brother and also a sister, who contracted encephalitis that resulted in brain damage.

1958

DECEMBER
Denny graduates from the University of Minnesota with a degree in psychology and is recruited for a one-year training program for Armstrong Cork, after which he is assigned the Southern Michigan selling territory.

1954

Denny graduates from Saint Paul Central High School.

in this new role. Already experienced in sales, having worked for many years in his father's wholesale clothing business, it was a comfortable environment for him, and represented a chance to refine and grow his existing skills. He earned a plum assignment—half of Detroit and Southern Michigan, then a vibrant marketplace. He quickly proved his business acumen and work ethic, closing deals consistently.

Denny, father of two sons, Bill and Scott, introduces them to the adventures he enjoys, including skiing. He is about 31 years old at the time of this ski trip.

His salary was $425 a month. Even after bringing the company its largest customer to date, when he asked his superiors for a $50 raise because he was about to get married, the answer was "No." There were policies regarding when an employee could receive a raise and for how much, he was told. "Policy schmolicy," Denny responded. "If I'm going to work, I'm going to make a good living for my family."

"I left and became a manufacturers' representative. ... I loved the idea of selling or promoting products to architects on large commercial, industrial buildings. Then [I] founded a manufacturers' rep company and became a distribution company of construction materials nationwide and then, ultimately, a manufacturing company. So, I vertically integrated on down to the basic, core products, and I took that public and did an IPO in 1972 at five dollars

1986

Having divorced and returned to Minnesota, Denny buys First Interstate Bank for $5 million from a friend needing to sell the bank quickly. He renames it First PREMIER Bank and seeks to rejuvenate it for greater profitability and visibility.

1972

Denny takes Contech, the company he started, public at $5 a share. Ten years later, with 350 employees and $35 million in sales, he sells his remaining interest. His take is $20 million, and at age 45 he retires to Florida but remains an active venture investor, using his newfound free time to lower his golf handicap to five.

a share, sold it in 1982 at $35 a share, so I had a lot of very, very happy shareholders."[12] It was evidence of a trend: extraordinary growth in the size and value of every business he touched. Denny had an uncanny ability to spot opportunities, to envision what it would take to achieve profitability, and to be able to articulate and enact those things with single-minded determination.[13] With the cash bundle from that sale, Denny formed Threshold Ventures, a venture capital company, and pulled back a bit from his 14-hour days.

Denny felt no particular desire to become deeply involved in running a company again, but in 1986, he received a call from a friend going through a divorce and in need of a quick purchase of a bank in Sioux Falls, South Dakota.[14] Denny agreed to step up, a decision that eventually changed the course of his future, his home base, even the entire consumer credit industry … and a leading health care system that would bear his name.

Denny knew he did not have the typical banker's mind-set but he suspected he would turn it over quickly once he had brought it from sleepy virtual invisibility to better performance. Then while brainstorming with colleagues, "the light went on," Denny said. "Sioux Falls, South Dakota, happens to be the credit card capital of the US, so let's explore that. I wound up hiring top people from Citibank and put together a great little organization—First PREMIER Bank and PREMIER Bankcard, and that worked out extremely well. That's primarily where the resources came from to support Sanford Health."[15]

"He wanted performance. We had to do things right," said Miles Beacom, president and CEO of PREMIER Bankcard,[16] the executive who launched

Today a major player in consumer credit and banking, First PREMIER Bank and PREMIER Bankcard were shoestring operations in the early days. *(Used with permission from First PREMIER Bank.)*

1999

APRIL 26
Denny pledges up to $2 million in matching funds to grow the endowment of Children's Home Society of South Dakota, which provides a continuum of services for children with emotional or behavioral problems, primarily associated with abuse and neglect.

USED WITH PERMISSION FROM FIRST PREMIER BANK.

PHOTO COURTESY OF THE CHILDREN'S HOME SOCIETY.

1989

OCTOBER 2
Seeking growth opportunities for the bank, Denny hires Miles Beacom from Citibank. Hoping to use South Dakota laws favorable to credit card companies to their advantage, they experiment with various approaches, eventually settling on offering premium-rate credit cards to people with poor credit ratings. Within months they have millions of cardholders, and First PREMIER Bankcard operations grow from 80 employees to more than 3,000.

Denny with PREMIER Bankcard
and First PREMIER Bank
executives Miles Beacom (left)
and Dana Dykhouse (right).

and runs the credit card operation on behalf of Denny to this day. It has become a major player in consumer credit and banking, but it was a shoestring operation in the early days. Denny's standard response, when Beacom made the pitch for more equipment and people: "You make some money, we'll upgrade."[17]

"It was tough ... but it was good as well," Beacom said. "He held us accountable for plans, for actions, for opportunities down the line. He wanted to make sure we weren't stubbing our toes and doing the wrong thing. ... He likes growth."[18]

"He enjoys seeing people succeed," said Dana Dykhouse, First PREMIER Bank's CEO.

During the next 25 years, that operation grew from 80 employees to more than 3,000, becoming so successful that 1995 records showed Denny to be worth $55 million,

---

2004

JANUARY 31
The Sioux Valley Foundation announces a lead gift of $16 million from Denny to build a new state-of-the-art children's hospital. "It's a great cause. This should help Sioux Valley and the community," Denny said. The hospital would be named Sanford Children's Hospital and marked the beginning of the dynamic relationship between Denny and Kelby Krabbenhoft.

USED WITH PERMISSION FROM THE
SIOUX EMPIRE UNITED WAY.

2001

DECEMBER 13
Denny presents the largest monetary gift ever to the Sioux Empire United Way: $100,000 to help serve the community's social service needs. In 1997, Denny was a founding donor to the Sioux Falls chapter of the Alexis de Tocqueville Society, a group of philanthropists who give at least $10,000 annually to the United Way.

A great adventurer who has been involved in all manner of athletic pursuits, Denny is a sailor who enjoys time out on the water.

and a decade later, in 2006, *Forbes* placed his fortune at $2.5 billion and named him the 117TH richest man in America.[19]

That Denny was entrepreneurial and clever, a very hard worker who took great pleasure in urging performance from acceptable to excellent, was obvious, but the additional layering of other qualities and interests were what made him not just another wealthy businessman, but an individual of depth and substance.

Known to friends and colleagues as a jokester and ceaseless competitor,[20] Denny played as hard as he worked, from racing sailboats in his early days to skiing at the best resorts around the world and golfing the most challenging courses. Still, he never lost his Upper Midwestern sensibilities, remaining through it all a fast-food aficionado who had to be reminded by colleagues to buy new cars when old ones became hideously road-worn, and a man who, when he held business retreats at his Arizona vacation home, cooked breakfast for the people who worked for him and arranged for such "highbrow" activities as bike rides and evening card games.[21]

"You sit down in a restaurant or at a basketball game with him, you'd never understand or know the [wealth] of that man," said Beacom. At lunchtime, he doesn't head for the club, he prefers "the local cafeteria and he likes to walk around and talk to the people."[22]

2005

DECEMBER 14
Denny donates $15 million to the Mayo Clinic to establish The Sanford Pediatric Center, an outpatient pediatric center in downtown Rochester, Minnesota. Of the amount, $5 million will create a research and information-exchange partnership between doctors at Mayo and at Sioux Valley Hospital. It is the largest gift to pediatric medicine in the clinic's history.

2005

NOVEMBER 11
The William Sanford Welcome Center at Bethesda Hospital in Saint Paul, Minnesota, is dedicated. Denny donated $500,000 to the long-term, acute-care hospital where he and other family members were born and received medical care. The name "William" was carried by his grandfather, his father, one of his sons, and his grandson.

Though a serious and uncompromising businessman, Denny's humanity and compassion have always been evident and genuine. Chuck remembers an older brother who was always willing to coach his baseball teams and engage in horseplay, eager to do for his little brother the things their father, who had a bad heart and was on doctor's orders to restrict activities, could not.

"He was not just the big brother, but the man-type figure," Chuck recalled. When their father died of a ruptured aorta while Denny was a student at the University of Minnesota, Denny rushed into his younger brother's bedroom, wrapped his arms around the 11-year-old, and stayed there, the two of them crying together, demonstrating "a bond that could never be broken," Chuck recalled.[23]

The same things that had been important to Denny in his youth, while he was struggling to make his way despite early heartache and disadvantage, continued to be important to him later in life. He treasured and extended the courtesies of honesty and straightforwardness to those he met along the way.

"His relationships are premised on some great, down-home values that are just DNA deep in him. ... He can size up substance and sincerity real quick," said Kelby Krabbenhoft, who enjoys knowing Denny as a successful benefactor on the path to giving donations and challenge grants to organizations in such large amounts that his name would eventually be on a medical school, a facility at his alma mater, a massive Midwest health care system, and several other operations scattered across several states.[24]

The local Sioux Falls, South Dakota, newspaper runs a story on Denny long before his donations became so stratospheric that they would make the local community and the world take notice. *(Reprinted with permission from the Argus Leader.)*

He rose from humble beginnings to become a South Dakota banking leader. Now he's investing in his own legacy by giving to others.

THE QUIET MILLIONAIRE

T. Denny Sanford is shown Aug. 2 at First Premier Bank in Sioux Falls, which he bought from a friend in 1986 when it was United National Bank. Sanford has been a behind-the-scenes benefactor to charities and causes in Sioux Falls.

BY KELLY HILDEBRANDT
ARGUS LEADER

2006

JUNE 21

A groundbreaking ceremony is held for a new 140,000-square-foot building in northwest Sioux Falls for PREMIER Bankcard. In making the announcement Denny says the company will be hiring as many as 500 additional employees over the next three to five years, bolstering the 2,550 PREMIER already employs throughout the state.

SANFORD SCHOOL OF MEDICINE
The University of South Dakota

USED WITH PERMISSION FROM THE SANFORD SCHOOL OF MEDICINE OF THE UNIVERSITY OF SOUTH DAKOTA.

2005

DECEMBER 27

Denny donates $20 million through Sioux Valley Hospitals and Health System to the University of South Dakota School of Medicine, and university officials announce that a new name will be in effect immediately: the Sanford School of Medicine at the University of South Dakota. This would be just the first of several contributions to the university.

In 1997 Denny kicked off the United Way of Sioux Falls' local Alexis de Tocqueville Society with a donation of $10,000, leading to more than 100 such gifts annually from other contributors.

Before Denny had amassed a fortune or began to make multimillion dollar donations, he had begun presenting some significant contributions—and showed where his heart lay—to organizations that help children and the disadvantaged. A longtime supporter of the Sioux Empire United Way, in 1997 Denny kicked off its local Alexis de Tocqueville Society with a donation of $10,000. The de Tocqueville Society is a group of United Way philanthropic leaders who contribute at least that amount annually to their local United Way. His first $10,000 was the largest contribution by an individual that had ever been made to the Sioux Empire United Way, and today the Sioux Empire de Tocqueville Society has more than 100 members.

Two years later in 1999, he pledged up to $2 million in matching money for the Children's Home Society in Sioux Falls, to support its school and home for children with emotional and behavioral needs associated with abuse and neglect. Denny had often stated that he wanted to be able to help provide early assistance to children who would not otherwise have the means or ability to get the kind of start in life that would allow them to be happy and successful. "They asked me for a million and I gave them two. I got sold by actually seeing what they did. You know, these are kids who are legally separated from their families. ... They live full time within the facility, and they're given an opportunity to have a nice, clean existence, in contrast to the physical and emotional or sexual abuse they've had to put up with," said Denny.[25] After that, the organization "needed an endowment consideration, so I spent a significant amount of money for that program."[26] He would continue to support the society regularly through subsequent donations.

2006

OCTOBER 18
Forbes magazine ranks Denny at No. 117 on its annual list of "400 Richest Americans." The magazine places Denny's worth at approximately $2.5 billion.

2006

AUGUST 6
Denny makes a gift of $14 million to the Children's Home Society in Sioux Falls. "The best investment that I can make is in children's lives because that's where the growth is going to come, that's where our communities' futures are going to come from. If we get children started on the right foot a lot of the ills of society go away," he says.

Denny is a gregarious sort who enjoys working any crowd. He feels a special affiliation with children, and much of the hundreds of millions of dollars he has given away has benefited kids.

2007

FEBRUARY 3
Krabbenhoft announces Denny's commitment of $400 million to Sioux Valley Hospitals and Health System to benefit and advance health care and medical research regionally, nationally, and internationally with clinics, cutting-edge research, and education. Concurrent with the announcement, the health system's name is changed to Sanford Health.

2006

NOVEMBER 20
Denny makes his first appearance on *BusinessWeek*'s 50 Most Generous Philanthropists. The magazine calculated his donations at an estimated $159 million since 2002, which placed him number 49 on its annual list.

Sanford
Health

Among the many who took notice of Denny's gift to help build the children's hospital was Laura Bush, First Lady at the time, who took the time to send a letter.

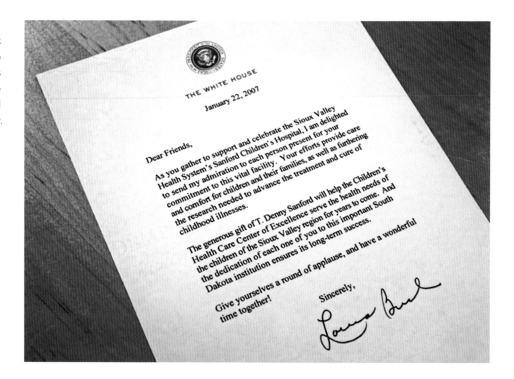

THE WHITE HOUSE

January 22, 2007

Dear Friends,

As you gather to support and celebrate the Sioux Valley Health System's Sanford Children's Hospital, I am delighted to send my admiration to each person present for your commitment to this vital facility. Your efforts provide care and comfort for children and their families, as well as furthering the research needed to advance the treatment and cure of childhood illnesses.

The generous gift of T. Denny Sanford will help the Children's Health Care Center of Excellence serve the health needs of the children of the Sioux Valley region for years to come. And the dedication of each one of you to this important South Dakota institution ensures its long-term success.

Give yourselves a round of applause, and have a wonderful time together!

Sincerely,

Laura Bush

His giving escalated, primarily to Upper Midwest causes he believed in, mostly to child- and health-related organizations—perhaps not surprisingly, given that not only had his mother died of cancer when he was a boy, but his father also suffered an untimely death due to heart disease. He also demonstrated, as time went on, an affection for supporting educational efforts, and, according to Dave Knudson, his long-time lawyer and facilitator of many of the contributions, for "things that will have an economic impact on the area."[27]

2007

FEBRUARY 4

Following the announcement of The Gift, the *Argus Leader* reports that South Dakota economist Randall Stuefen predicts Denny's $400 million gift will generate thousands of jobs and will drive $1.15 billion in economic development for the area in the next decade.

2007

FEBRUARY 8

The *Chronicle of Philanthropy* does a cover story on Denny and says his $400 million contribution is the largest ever for health care organizations.

Investing in Society's Future

Though Denny Sanford's most notable contributions have been to Sanford Health, there have been scores of others in the last decade, most of them focused toward children, medical research, and education.

Among the largest include $70 million in 2006 for the Homestake Gold Mine in Lead, South Dakota, to fund renovations in preparation for receiving a National Science Foundation designation as an underground physics lab. The laboratory was renamed the Sanford Underground Science and Engineering Laboratory at Homestake, and $20 million of that amount was earmarked for the creation of the Sanford Center for Science Education to connect the site to scientists, educators, students, and the public. Recounted former South Dakota governor Mike Rounds:

[Denny] said, "I think we ought to move forward with that laboratory because I think it's long-term, it's the right thing to do." And I said, I agree, but you know I need the National Science Foundation on board with us in order to fund the project and right now they're not doing it. He says, "Well, I think we ought to build it." And I said, "I'm glad you agree with me, but right now we're kind of hung up in that we've got to be able to get the funds to do it." He said, "You don't understand. I don't think we should wait on Washington on this. This is too important. I will give you the 50 million dollars to fund that program." [1]

Other sizeable gifts have included $20 million to expand educational programming at the University of South Dakota School of Medicine; $30 million to the San Diego Consortium for Regenerative Medicine (renamed the Sanford Consortium for Regenerative Medicine) to help people with life-altering and debilitating diseases; and $20 million to the Burnham Institute for Medical Research in La Jolla, California, to create the Sanford Children's Health Research Center collaboration with Sanford Health.[2] Denny also established a large lead challenge gift to the now Sanford-Burnham Institute.

He presented $15 million to the Mayo Clinic—$10 million for a new pediatric outpatient facility and $5 million to create a collaboration between Sanford Children's Hospital and the Mayo Clinic,[3] and in a series of donations, more than $18 million to Arizona State University to attract, train, and retrain effective school teachers.[4]

Denny also contributed a vital $5 million to the School of Business at the University of South Dakota to kick off a building fund drive. "It would have been very difficult if not impossible to construct that building without that $5 million lead gift, because our state isn't funding buildings," said Jim Abbott, president of the University of South Dakota. Denny was granted naming rights, but instead of putting his own name on it, he designated it the Beacom School to honor Miles Beacom, the man who made PREMIER Bankcard into such a success. "And lately," said Abbott, "in the last few years, we've expanded health sciences quite a bit. ... Denny Sanford's gift for the Sanford School of Medicine further strengthens our partnership with Sanford Health." Sanford Health has a long-standing, close relationship with the University of South Dakota (USD) and trains many of the medical and nursing students that are enrolled at USD. The former Sioux Valley hospital is now Sanford USD Medical Center.

Some of Denny's gifts have been smaller, but no less impactful for the organizations that received them, including $4 million to the Roundup River Ranch in Vail, Colorado, a camp for children with life-threatening illnesses, with $3 million pledged in matching funds; $1 million to his fraternity Chi Psi at the University of Minnesota to renovate the fraternity house; and $4.5 million, with another $4.5 million in matching funds, for the Crazy Horse Memorial in the Black Hills of South Dakota.[5]

"I look at life as an investor," Denny said, "vetting charitable donations based on which will give the best return, which will accomplish the most good for the money."

"To invest in the health and well-being of children is to seek the greatest return we can hope to achieve," stated Denny Sanford, pictured here with Ben Calsbeek, a type 1 diabetes patient, at the Sanford Project announcement.

Denny's first effort to make a major contribution, $35 million to help his alma mater build a new football stadium, did not pan out when discussions about the particulars reached a stalemate. He had a strong conviction that a recipient of such a large amount of money should be willing to take advice from the giver and should also demonstrate willingness to be a solid steward of the money. Throughout his philanthropy, he remained consistent, providing well-received and welcome advice along with his contribution and encouragement.

The inability to reach an acceptable agreement in the stadium deal did not in any way diminish his desire to give. When Krabbenhoft made his first official contact with Denny in 2003 to request $16 million as the fund-raising kickoff to build a long-dreamed-for children's hospital, Denny responded affirmatively almost immediately.

Denny with Krabbenhoft, Becky Nelson, and David Link, together representing the visionary leadership and incredible philanthropy that transformed how the future of Sanford Health would materialize and be carried through.

"It was a major gift," recalled former governor Mike Rounds. "It woke people up to the fact that Denny Sanford was clearly interested in participating in children's health. It also suggested that one person could truly make a difference."[28]

Unveiled in 2009, the children's hospital bearing Denny's name was the first of what would be called "Castle of Care" facilities,

2007

NOVEMBER 18
Denny pledges $20 million to establish the Sanford Children's Health Research Center, a joint venture of Sanford Health and the Burnham Institute for Medical Research in La Jolla, California.

2007

NOVEMBER 23
Denny is named the 17ᵀᴴ most generous giver in *BusinessWeek*'s annual list of top philanthropists. The magazine reports he has pledged $559 million in his lifetime. His level of giving turned out to actually be higher than that reported by the magazine, said the Associated Press, as he had recently given $20 million to the Burnham Institute for Medical Research and $5 million to South Dakota State University's Dykhouse Student Athlete Center.

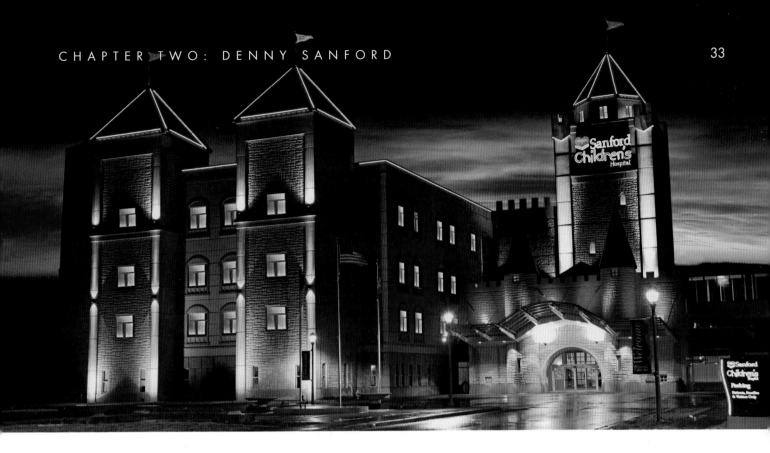

designed and built with careful attention to every detail, faithful to Krabbenhoft's belief that the right architecture was vital to creating a healing environment. The Castle of Care design ensures children and families are not intimidated, but rather feel eager to enter and that they would have positive memories of an experience that all too often seems terrifying.

Denny's donation to that hospital turned out to be the first step on a shared journey with Krabbenhoft and the health care organization that would ultimately

Sanford Children's Castle of Care in Sioux Falls has 146 beds and is also home to Sanford Children's Specialty Clinic, with 38 exam rooms and a designated space for pediatric cancer patients to receive treatment, all designed to meet the unique needs of children.

2008

FEBRUARY 3

Denny ties for third place in the ranking of the 50 most generous Americans compiled by the *Chronicle of Philanthropy*, which attributes the ranking in large part to the $400 million pledge to Sanford Health.

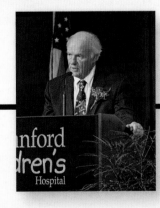

Denny's generous donations to health care organizations would lead to his name being bestowed upon health care facilities across several states, including the Sanford School of Medicine of the University of South Dakota. *(Photo courtesy of the Sanford School of Medicine of the University of South Dakota.)*

alter his life and lead to his name being bestowed upon health care facilities across several states and even throughout the world—not just at Sanford Health, but also at renowned facilities such as the T. Denny Sanford Pediatric Center at the Mayo Clinic, the William Sanford Welcome Center at Bethesda Hospital in Saint Paul, Minnesota (the hospital where he had been born decades earlier), and the Sanford School of Medicine at the University of South Dakota.[29]

Denny donated so much to various worthy causes that he was ranked by the *Chronicle of Philanthropy* as the nation's 14TH most generous donor for 2005, a year in which he gave away $70 million.[30]

In 2007, the biggest donation of them all was announced: $400 million to what would thereafter be known as Sanford Health, a system of 24 hospitals and 115 clinics. The goal was nothing less than curing a devastating disease and transforming the way health care was delivered across the region, nationally, and on a global scale.

2009

NOVEMBER 2
Sanford Health becomes the largest rural integrated health care system in the nation following the merger of Sanford Health and MeritCare Health System.

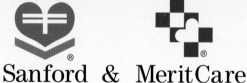

Sanford Health & MeritCare

Stronger Together

2008

NOVEMBER 25
Denny is No. 15 on *BusinessWeek's* Top 50 American Philanthropists. The magazine points out he "pledged $44 million in charitable contributions in 2008, including donating $30 million to the San Diego Consortium for Regenerative Medicine, which was rebranded the Sanford Consortium for Regenerative Medicine."

"If I could put my name on a project in my lifetime and see a major medical breakthrough because of it, that's what I would love to do," Denny told reporters at the announcement. "The idea that we could really put Sioux Falls and South Dakota so much more on the map, that we could create additional employment and attract people from around the country and around the world, that was really a hot button for me."[31] On June 5, 2008, such a project, The Sanford Project to cure type 1 diabetes, was announced.

As Denny approaches his eighth decade of life, he still keeps a hand in his businesses, rotating between his home in South Dakota, and vacation homes in Colorado, Arizona, and California, and attacks life with gusto, referring to himself as the "WOLT—world's oldest living teenager."[32]

The father of sons Scott and Bill is also a regular attendee at Sanford Health's children's galas, its groundbreakings, and other events marking the progress of the organization. "Dad is a man of his word. His generosity is based on what and who he believes in," says son Bill Sanford.

The people he encounters often say the same thing about him, remarking on his warmth and friendliness. "You can see people's faces light up when they interact with him and the awe [when] they've never seen him in person before," said Brian Mortenson. "To them, he's a bit larger than life and yet he's a regular guy, too, so it's kind of a blessed combination."[33]

Denny continues to contribute to causes and organizations he believes in, also signing the Giving Pledge in 2012 that was established two years earlier by Warren Buffet and Bill

Brian Mortenson is president of the Sanford Health Foundation and was key to facilitating The Gift from Denny.

2010

SEPTEMBER 10
The University of Minnesota's T. Denny Sanford Athletics Hall of Fame, a 5,000-square-foot center that commemorates all Gopher sports with photographs, artifacts, and interactive kiosks, opens in the new stadium, which was built with $6 million donated by Denny in May 2009.

T. DENNY SANFORD
UNIVERSITY OF MINNESOTA
ATHLETICS HALL OF FAME

2010

JANUARY 29
Denny issues a $50 million matching gift challenge benefiting Burnham Institute for Medical Research, to accelerate its research. It is Denny's second gift to Burnham, the first being $20 million in 2007 directed through Sanford Health to create the Sanford Children's Health Research Center at Burnham. With the second gift, the organization is renamed the Sanford-Burnham Medical Research Institute.

Sanford|Burnham
Medical Research Institute

Joining Denny in celebrating the events of the day at the February 3, 2007, Children's Gala are, left to right, Denny's daughter-in-law, Andrea, and sons Bill and Scott.

and Melinda Gates to encourage the wealthiest to give away most of their fortunes to philanthropy before they die, or to arrange for it to be given to charities soon after their deaths. Dennis Daugaard, governor of South Dakota, said this about Denny:

> *The booming health care sector, along with the growth in financial services [have been important] for South Dakota. At the intersection of the health care and financial services industries is Denny Sanford, whose [career with First PREMIER Bank] presaged a second career as one of the nation's largest philanthropists.*[34]

2011

AUGUST 17
Sanford Health announces Denny's Edith Sanford Breast Cancer gift of $100 million at a special community event.

2011

JULY 22
The Sanford "*fit*" program in partnership with WebMD and Disney is implemented, providing parents, children, and health professionals resources to promote healthy lifestyles in children.

"I'm running out of the runway of my life," says Denny often, "and my preference is to die broke."[35]

Denny has accomplished a significant place in the business world of today, and his legacy as a remarkable philanthropist is well established. His gifts to his primary philanthropic interest—Sanford Health—now total $600 million and have indeed been transformational. In actual and in "today's dollars," they are greater than the gifts that underpinned iconic institutions such as Johns Hopkins and Mayo Clinic. Through unique initiatives made possible by Denny's contributions and a growing footprint, an enduring signature effect such as Carnegie's can be seen in an increasing number of communities across the Upper Midwest, other states, and around the world where locations for vital health care services carry the name Sanford. Together, Sanford Health and Denny continue to pursue "making a real difference in people's lives" and improving the human condition.

2011

SUMMER 2011

Denny's gifts to Sanford Health since 2004 total $600 million, transforming the organization and its health care, research, and education endeavors in ways that are nationally recognized and world changing. These include Sanford Children's Hospital, Sanford School of Medicine, The Gift, Sanford Children's Health Research Center, Sanford *fit* program, and the Edith Sanford Breast Cancer Foundation.

2012

Denny is named Outstanding International Philanthropist of 2012 by the Association of Fundraising Professionals.

PHOTO: © STEVEN E. PURCELL

2012

Denny is selected for the University of Minnesota Alumni Achievement Award.

CHAPTER THREE

KELBY K. KRABBENHOFT—
THE MAN WITH A PLAN

Our intent is to change the course of things. By committing our organization to a grand cause,
we can arrive at that place called significance. You today witness the improving of the human
condition; the wonder of the generosity of a man whose gift could change the world, the
affirmation of being "dedicated to the work of healing" and turning hope into reality.

—Kelby Krabbenhoft
announcing Denny Sanford's gift and the name change to Sanford Health[1]

Above: A young Kelby Krabbenhoft develops his passion for the medical field after his brother is paralyzed by a fall from a tree and Krabbenhoft spends weeks with him in the hospital.

Opposite: Krabbenhoft announces The Gift. Krabbenhoft has completely reshaped the health care landscape in the Upper Midwest with his vision, personal warmth, and character.

TALL AND CHARISMATIC WITH A BLEND OF UPPER MIDWEST SENSIBILITIES and big city ambition, Kelby Krabbenhoft had little trouble winning over the Sioux Valley Hospital board of directors when he arrived in Sioux Falls to apply for the position of CEO in 1996. At 39, he was a younger-than-usual candidate for such an important position, but he had risen quickly up the health care ranks in various successful positions of importance throughout the Upper Midwest, earning a reputation as a creative, hard-driving, no-nonsense leader. He was immediately liked by the board of trustees, due to a straightforward Dakotas sensibility, a good fit for Sioux Falls, with the background and the ambitions they were seeking.

Born in Iowa and raised in Mankato, Minnesota, Krabbenhoft also lived in New Mexico and Oregon as his father completed his doctoral studies in microbiology.[2] Summers were spent at his father's and mother's family farms near Northwood, North Dakota, establishing an early connection to the area that would be part of the "Dakota Territory" served by Sanford Health. It was there on those North Dakota farms that Krabbenhoft developed a keen ability to work with others and took the lead as a horse wrangler amongst his many duties.

As a teenager, Krabbenhoft had a life-changing experience after his younger brother was paralyzed falling from a tree and spent four months in the University of Minnesota Medical Center. There, when he visited his brother day after day, Krabbenhoft encountered the work and dedication to healing of the hospital, its doctors, nurses, and therapists, leading to an

Right: Krabbenhoft spent his formative high school and college years in Mankato and Moorhead, Minnesota.

Below: Krabbenhoft spent summers on his family's farms in North Dakota. He developed a special knack for working with horses.

abiding desire to be involved in health care delivery. It also set in place an indelible impression of the impact that design and substance in hospital architecture has on patients and family, which would be seen later in the "Health Care Campus of the Future" planning he would lead. During his visits, Krabbenhoft witnessed and is still moved by the memory of the sad conditions of children born to mothers who had contracted rubella before vaccinations were available. This formed the basis for his commitment to research and the pursuit of cures and his becoming a driving force in such future-oriented initiatives as The Sanford Project.

1957

DECEMBER 14

Kelby K. Krabbenhoft is born in Ames, Iowa, the son of a college professor and a school teacher. The family soon moves to Mankato, Minnesota, where his father teaches microbiology and young Kelby will spend his childhood and adolescence.

1969

Krabbenhoft resolves to go into health care delivery as a young man after experiencing the sad conditions of neonatal rubella victims when visiting his brother in the hospital after he became paralyzed falling from a tree.

A typical middle-class youth with jobs that ranged from farm work to the coveted position of ball boy at the Minnesota Vikings training camp, Krabbenhoft started college with the goal of attending medical school. When organic chemistry proved not to be his strong suit, he set his sights on the business side of health care. More summer jobs such as a shoe salesman at J.C. Penney and a roofer gave him important, if quite different, insights into connecting with people of diverse backgrounds.

An excellent student and talented basketball player at Concordia College in Moorhead, Minnesota, it was under the tutelage of a venerable professor of hospital administration, Ted Heimarck, that Krabbenhoft began his quest for making a difference in health care. He would graduate with a degree in hospital administration and go on to earn a master's degree in business administration at Minnesota State University in Mankato.[3]

Equipped with credentials and determination, Krabbenhoft dove into his career unsure how it would all unfold, absorbing every detail, learning as he advanced, forming strong ideas about the weaknesses of the health system and beginning to envision what it would take to create a comprehensive, forward-thinking, patient-centered, physician-run approach that could ultimately transform lives.

He advanced through executive positions in Iowa, Illinois, and North Dakota, eventually becoming president and CEO of Freeman Health System in Joplin, Missouri.[4] While in Missouri, Krabbenhoft grew Freeman from one hospital to a system of three, and oversaw the successful launches of sophisticated heart and cancer programs. Those bold and pioneering accomplishments impressed the board in Sioux Falls during his candidate interviews.

1980

JUNE

Krabbenhoft graduates from Concordia College, having played forward for the basketball team. Decades later he will accept an invitation to join the college's prestigious board of trustees and the Offutt School of Business Leadership Council, consisting of top leaders from major companies.

1982

JUNE

Continuing to prepare for a career in health care, Krabbenhoft receives his MBA in his hometown of Mankato, after having studied for two years at Mankato State University, now known as Minnesota State University Mankato. He was selected for their Alumni Achievement Award in 2007.

Sioux Valley
Health System

Draft – Press Release
President/CEO Sioux Valley Health System

For immediate release:
October 15, 1996

Sioux Valley Health System President Named

The Sioux Valley Health System Board of Directors announced Tuesday that Kelby
Krabbenhoft has been appointed President/Chief Executive Officer of the Sioux Va
Health System. Mr. Krabbenhoft is currently serving as President/CEO of Freema
Health System in Joplin, Missouri. The Freeman Health System is a three-hospita
organization with other affiliated hospitals that serve portions of a four-state regi
which includes Missouri, Kansas, Oklahoma and Arkansas. Krabbenhoft came t
Freeman System from Fargo, North Dakota where he was Executive Vice Presi
the six-hospital, Sisters of Mary of the Presentation Health System. The 38-yea
native of Mankato, Minnesota received his education at Concordia College an
State University.

1994, *Modern Healthcare's Up and Comer* named him one of America's le
ecutives. He is currently in his second term as Chairman of the
Hospitals of America.   will lead a growing

His knowledge of, and commitment to, the notion of integrated health care, which
Sioux Valley Hospital had already begun to implement, propelled him ahead of the
other candidates.

Krabbenhoft arrived in Sioux Valley Hospital on his first day full of energy and ideas,
eager to get the ball rolling. Everyone in the organization would eventually learn that his
potency, endurance, and impatience were boundless, but Krabbenhoft had the prudence
to temper his hard-charging ways at the outset.

1982

Krabbenhoft takes his first full-time job in the health care industry
as president and CEO of a small rural hospital (40 beds and
$3 million in revenue) in Guttenberg, Iowa.

1984

Krabbenhoft here confers with his father in his new
position as president and CEO of St. Margaret's Hospital
in Spring Valley, Illinois, a larger (188-bed) facility.

As Krabbenhoft sat at an event watching while the revered, retiring CEO Lyle Schroeder, with 36 years in the position, said his good-byes to the assembled staff, the new CEO sensed something important in the air and made a midstep alteration, deciding to depart from his plan for that night.

Krabbenhoft realized this organization had a rich and successful tradition many decades old, and a sense of pride in what it had accomplished. Now was not the time to disgorge all his plans and big ideas for the future. Doing so would have been "distracting and aggressive" under the circumstances.[5] When he took the stage, he explained what he thought most important. "I've just been given a precious egg, this egg, and my No. 1 job is don't drop the egg. Don't drop the egg," he said, with his characteristic spirit. [6]

He went on to say much more, little of it scripted. Most of it "honored those people who birthed that egg."[7] His ability to quickly evaluate the social, political, and emotional atmosphere would become a Krabbenhoft trademark in the years to come.

Krabbenhoft felt strongly that momentum and growth were vital to the health system accomplishing its full potential. "The integration of physicians was key," he said, because "in my mind, I wanted one of the biggest clinics in the country. You've got to have it to do what needs to be done for patient care."[8]

"I had this ache" to charge forth on this goal, he said, but he did not want to jeopardize the "precious pride in this organization." He realized it would take time before new directions would not be seen as threatening or disruptive.

Krabbenhoft rolled up his sleeves and methodically began to build relationships.

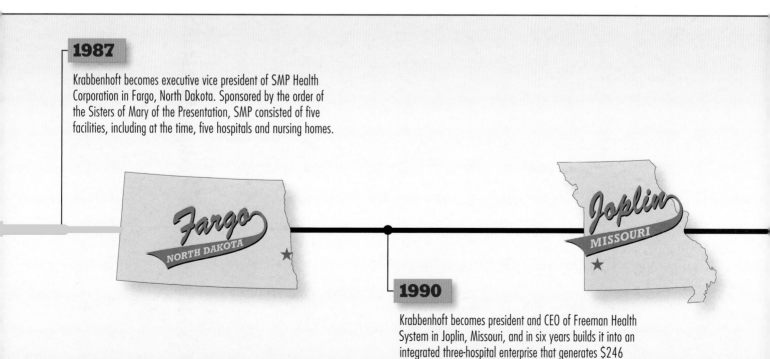

1987

Krabbenhoft becomes executive vice president of SMP Health Corporation in Fargo, North Dakota. Sponsored by the order of the Sisters of Mary of the Presentation, SMP consisted of five facilities, including at the time, five hospitals and nursing homes.

1990

Krabbenhoft becomes president and CEO of Freeman Health System in Joplin, Missouri, and in six years builds it into an integrated three-hospital enterprise that generates $246 million in annual revenue.

At the time, an issue was brewing, for which the resolution would be a key development in Krabbenhoft's early career with Sioux Valley Hospital and for the organization itself. The issue involved the existing private cardiology group wanting to use a then loophole in the Stark Law to "carve out" traditional and core hospital service revenue for their benefit without regard for the negative impact that it would have on Sioux Valley Hospital's ability to maintain its overall patient service levels.

It was also contrary to the Sioux Valley Hospital integration model under development. Krabbenhoft, the Sioux Valley Hospital physician group, and his executive team with the support of the board of trustees, stood strong against such a proposed arrangement, and as a result, the private cardiac group left to start its own limited service, physician-owned hospital. This put Krabbenhoft in the position of needing to develop a Sioux Valley Hospital cardiac physican group. The group was assembled and launched, and over the next 15 years, the growth, program enhancements, and service initiatives culminated in the recent addition of a dedicated, state-of-the-art heart hospital as part of the Sioux Falls Sanford USD Medical Center comprehensive health care facilities.

The experience also led to Krabbenhoft becoming a leader in the national hospital industry. He led the way for the formation of the Coalition of Full Service Community Hospitals, which manned the oars in addressing, at the national level, the unfairness of the Stark loophole and its adverse impact on community hospitals across America.

1994

AUGUST

Krabbenhoft is named an "Up & Comer" by *Modern Healthcare*. He is quoted as saying playing college basketball taught him how to be an underdog. "You start taking punches and not falling down." Twelve years later the same publication's collegiate-themed yearbook, following up on previous "Up and Comers," labels him a "star student."

A supplement to
Modern Healthcare

UP & COMERS YEARBOOK

CLASS OF THE HEALTHCARE INDUSTRY
1987-2006

Celebrating 20 years of rising young healthcare management talent

REPRINTED WITH PERMISSION, *MODERN HEALTHCARE.* © CRAIN COMMUNICATIONS, INC.

1996

MARCH 8

While hosting former British prime minister Margaret Thatcher (in red), keynote speaker at the prestigious Freeman Health System "Quality of Medicine" event, Krabbenhoft asks her, "How do you run your organization?" "You mean England?" she asked. "Yes. I'm most interested in how you deal with the queen because I have a board," he confided.

A Visionary Leader

From his earliest days in Sioux Falls, Kelby Krabbenhoft held the belief that a health institution that truly serves the community must combine research, academia, geographic expanse, a health plan, and an integrated health care delivery system.

An integrated health system combines physicians and hospitals in one organization working together to better coordinate care and improve quality, access, effectiveness, and efficiency in the delivery of comprehensive health services.[1] "We developed our integrated model because integration is the best way to deliver patient care," said Krabbenhoft.

The Sioux Valley Hospital had already begun the integration of about four dozen physicians into the facility before Krabbenhoft arrived in Sioux Falls, but integration was not fully embraced by all participants, or even by other leaders in the health care industry. "It was both exciting and a little bit … threatening in some cases to some groups … [who worried] what's this mean for us? Where's this going?" said Larry Toll, who was on the board when the physician integration discussions were in full swing.[2]

Around the country there was a widely held belief that integration was "just buying physician practices—a lot of organizations around the country were doing that for market-share reasons," recalled Senior Executive Vice President Dave Link.[3] Krabbenhoft and the board believed there was much more to it. "We needed to have all the pieces of the puzzle together— physicians, hospital, long-term care, the health plan, the financing aspect of it—if we were really going to be the best. If you looked around at the best organizations in

the country at the time, they were really all fully integrated organizations."[4]

Toll and Krabbenhoft attended a conference during those challenging days, and a speaker there commented that with integration "you really could take advantage of your doctors and particularly employed doctors like our model is here," Toll recalled. "And Kelby got really upset with this speaker and said … 'You know, if you take advantage of those doctors … the pendulum will swing back. They won't see it as a true partnership, and when it swings back, you know they're going to … get their day. This is about being in business together for all of us to be able to do better and provide better care for our patients.' "[5]

The integration efforts at Sioux Valley Hospital and later Sanford Health continued, and over time, the metrics pointed to success, concerns diminished, and the results were roundly applauded.

Year after year Sanford Health is recognized by IMS Health (previously SDI Health) as one of the nation's most integrated health care institutions according to 13 attributes, such as integrated information technology, financial stability, services, and access.[6]

Sanford Health also conducts its own basic and clinical research, and regularly collaborates with outside organizations to seek out cutting-edge solutions to medical challenges. It has relationships with several medical schools, institutes, and colleges, and many health professional training programs. Its geographic expanse has grown to more than 220,000 square miles, and it instituted its own successful health insurance plan within the first 24 months of Krabbenhoft's arrival in Sioux Falls.

1996

DECEMBER

Krabbenhoft arrives to take over Sioux Valley Hospital, having been selected from several candidates interviewed by the board of trustees during the summer and autumn of that year.

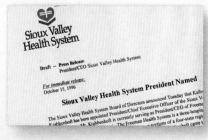

"He [Krabbenhoft] is one of those very rare individuals who has the vision, but also the drive to get it done," said Brian Mortenson, president of the Sanford Health Foundation.[9] He also had the wisdom to surround himself with the right people. "He really is a true leader [who] packs strong people around him ... so that they will challenge him or be able to guide him if it's not quite his expertise," said Barbara Stork, board of trustees member.[10]

Few, if any, in the organization had ever experienced such a determined leader as Krabbenhoft. "You just touch the accelerator and you ... do 360 [mph] down the expressway. He's very dynamic, very progressive, and very fast-moving," said longtime MeritCare board member and new Sanford Health trustee Jerome Feder.[11]

Tom Hruby served on the board of North Country Health Services and now is on the Sanford Health board of trustees.

"You see him as a person that can fill the room, not only with his size, but just the sense of his strong presence. A real individual that is a leader," said Rob Oliver, president of Augustana College and former president of Wells Fargo Bank in Sioux Falls. "Right away, you're impressed with the fact that this is a person that has a lot of capacity."[12]

"He's articulate," said Tom Hruby, who was on the board of North Country Health Services, which merged in 2011 with Sanford Health.[13] "He obviously is in command. ... He has a firm focus as to what he wants to do ... and he's just an impressive gentleman top to bottom."[14]

With time, almost everyone in the organization became convinced they could do anything Krabbenhoft told them they could. "I think that's what Kelby's been able to engender," said Sanford Health executive David Danielson. "[The idea is that] we're not yet finished, we've

1998

Through Krabbenhoft's leadership, the initial Sanford Research organization is formed with a commitment of $1 million per year for scientific discovery to enhance patient care.

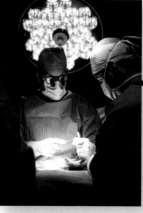

1999

Krabbenhoft and Becky Nelson form a plan for five "Centers of Excellence" to help lead Sioux Valley Hospitals and Health System's future development. The Centers include Heart, Cancer, Women's, Children's, and Ortho/Neuro/Trauma. Further specialization will be supported by new facilities.

got things to do, we have places to go, and that keeps us all hopping, and keeps us striving to do better."

"He's not afraid to stick his neck out and take risks," said two-time US Open championship golfer Andy North, recruited by Krabbenhoft to head up the Sanford Children's International Board. "And if the leader is willing to stick his neck out, it sure makes it much easier for the people underneath him to do that. He's created an environment ... in which

Two-time US Open championship golfer Andy North was recruited by Krabbenhoft to head up the Sanford Children's International Board.

A Giving Spirit

"Health systems must seek out donors large and small to support investments in the latest technology and the best talent to advance the organization's capabilities," Kelby Krabbenhoft has reminded many audiences.

Contributions from benefactors enable health systems to launch the research and cutting-edge approaches that can facilitate meaningful progress in the field.

By 1999, the year Brian Mortenson, now president of the Sanford Health Foundation, joined Sioux Valley Hospital, the hospital had developed a "good solid annual ... donor base and endowment activity" and "it was time to build a program around that," he recalled.[1] He suggested trying to get 100 people to commit to a personal named endowment fund of $10,000 or more, $25,000 or more for corporate entities within a two-year period.

Krabbenhoft personally made the first pledge and in just a few months many had committed more than $10,000 to build that next layer. The hospital began receiving six-figure gifts from the community, benefiting from the increased awareness enabled by Krabbenhoft, Mortenson, and their team.

"Henry and Eleanor Carlson and the late Al and Marion Egger were our two leaders from a donor perspective who established gift-giving levels which others viewed as leadership gifts," said Mortenson. Bob Locken took the philanthropic effort to the next level, with the first $1 million gift commitment.

"Kelby really put us on a new level of fund-raising capacity," Mortenson said. "He has an intuitive sense of understanding of things that can and should become rather iconic in the eyes and minds of the public, of doctors or of donors."[2]

The millions of dollars in gifts the Sanford Health Foundation received annually from benefactors allowed the organization to initiate many things that otherwise could not have happened, a prime example being the children's hospital.

When Denny Sanford gave his first $16 million to build the children's hospital, he wanted it to be used to leverage the additional millions necessary for the project, so Mortenson created "the Sanford Challenge," raising approximately $30 million over the next few years. The state-of-the-art Castle of Care Children's Hospital was completed and opened to the community in 2009.

2000

Sioux Valley Hospitals and Health System and the University of South Dakota establish an agreement for advancing medical education and the role of the hospital. Sioux Valley Hospital adds USD Medical Center to its name.

As soon as he arrived as Sioux Valley Hospital CEO, Krabbenhoft made it clear he believed philanthropic gifts to the hospital are necessary to move ahead certain types of programs and initiatives. In relatively short order, Al and Marion Egger gave $500,000 to the Sioux Valley Foundation to further research efforts undertaken jointly by Sioux Valley Hospital and the University of South Dakota School of Medicine. Robert Locken gave $1 million to establish an endowment to fund patient care initiatives. *(Newspaper articles reprinted with permission from the Argus Leader.)*

Family gives $500,000 to Sioux Valley, USD

By JOYCE TERVEEN
Argus Leader

Al and Marion Egger, longtime residents of Sioux Falls, have donated $500,000 to further research and education at Sioux Valley Hospital and the University of South Dakota School of Medicine.

It's the largest gift ever received by the Sioux Valley Foundation. The Eggers, honored Wednesday at a reception at the USD Health Science building in Sioux Falls, say the money is simply a way to say thanks.

"This community, and particularly the health-care community, has been really good to us and our families," said Al Egger, who 54 years ago founded the Egger Steel Co.

"Marion and I were both born in Minnehaha County a few years back. This has been our base all of our life," Al Egger said.

"Quite a few years back" added Marion Egger, smiling.

The couple, both near 90 years old, have been married 64 years. Their children, Steve Egger and Kathy Egger Schmidt, were born at Sioux Valley. And both Al and Marion Egger have been patients at the hospital.

Al Egger served as board chairman for Sioux Valley from 1986 to 1989, and has served as a member of the Sioux Valley Foundation Board of Directors.

The most recent donations bring the Eggers' contributions to Sioux Valley to $700,000 since 1991, when they established the Egger Research and Education Endowment Fund. Money from that fund already has funded research and education, including projects on medical conditions from endometriosis to arthritis.

The Eggers' latest contribution will be known as the Egger Research Development Institute. Funds from it are available for research for doctors, researchers and other staff in the medical school or Sioux Valley system, said Brian Mortenson, Sioux Valley Foundation president.

"There are people on site who think they are on to something, but they need to put a little more effort into what's working and what's not to see if their theories or ideas are correct," Mortenson said. "They may not be ready to go for a huge grant from the National Institutes of Health."

Grants that come from the Eggers' generosity could help budding research projects get started, Mortenson said.

Christopher Giannen / Argus Leader
Al and Marion Egger stand Wednesday on the Sioux Valley Hospital campus where a $500,000 donation was announced.

DEC 16 1999

$1M gift to Sioux Valley largest ever for hospital

By CORRINE OLSON
Argus Leader

The Sioux Valley Foundation has received a $1 million donation from a 70-year-old Sioux Falls man — the largest gift in the foundation's history.

Robert Locken, a retired Sioux Falls telephone company employee, officially will present his gift Wednesday.

Locken has set up a trust that will pay him an income until his death. When he dies, the trust will revert to the foundation.

"As I grow older, I see everyone starts to participate in the use of the hospital," Locken said, explaining his gift. "Over the years, I've used the hospital a lot. I've been very happy in Sioux Falls."

Locken, a widower, has lived in Sioux Falls for more than 30 years. He is a retired district manager for Northwestern Bell. He said he would like his donation to be used for medical education and children, but he has given hospital officials flexibility.

"I don't know how much longer I'll live," Locken said. "I don't know what the hospital is going to need at the time of my death."

Sioux Valley Foundation President Brian Mortenson said the foundation funds a variety of needs, including continuing education for staff, medical research and free medical procedures for people who can't afford them. Locken's gift will help pay those costs, he said.

This is the second large gift the foundation has received in recent months.

In December, Al and Marion Egger, longtime residents of Sioux Falls, donated $500,000 to further research and education at Sioux Valley Hospital and the University of South Dakota School of Medicine. At the time, it was the largest gift ever received by the foundation.

As thanks for Locken's generosity, the hospital's new lobby will be named the Robert A. Locken Lobby.

Locken likes that tribute.

"The lobby is where you come as a start of refuge, and it should be a place where people are greeted," he said. "Hopefully, when they get all done, they go through the lobby cured."

Reach reporter Corrine Olson at 331-2311 or colson@argusleader.com

2001

The merger of the Sioux Valley Physician Group and the Central Plains Clinic creates the largest physician group in the region. Krabbenhoft signs the merger agreement with Dr. T. A. Schultz, Central Plains Clinic board chair.

2002

Sioux Valley Hospitals and Health System opened the NORTH Center — bringing together ortho/neuro/rehab and sports medicine services.

everybody feels like they're a big part of the answer, and that they are very important to the success of the company."[15]

"Kelby," said Mark Glissendorf, senior vice president of Lawrence & Schiller, the Sioux Falls advertising firm Sanford Health began working with while it was still Sioux Valley Hospital, "is one of the fiercest competitors I've been around in my life. ... At the same time, he may be one of the most loyal individuals I've ever been around. If you will ... grab your sword and charge into battle beside Kelby, you have a friend for life."[16]

Nine years after arriving in Sioux Falls, Krabbenhoft sought and received a transformative contribution from Denny Sanford, who by then was convinced of his ability to deliver on his vision and plans.

Seeking and obtaining that donation may have been the gutsiest of his moves, certainly because of its sheer size. It actually surprised a few board members that he came up with the idea and carried it out. What he did, said former chair of the legacy Sanford Health board Stork, was to "sell a dream, a vision," because he had a sterling history and the ability to give Denny "the confidence that [as] the caretaker of that vision ... Kelby would make sure it will evolve and that the gift will be taken care of. There's not too much more you can say about a leader that can do that."[17]

His top leaders—his team—are stalwart standard-bearers possessing very nearly the same drive and energy as Krabbenhoft.

"The money might be there, but you can stretch your organization to the point where it starts breaking down," said Ron Moquist, member and first chair of the new

Barbara Stork served as vice chair of the board of Sioux Valley Hospitals and Health System when The Gift was established and chair of the Sanford Health board of trustees during the merger with MeritCare.

2003

Sioux Valley Cancer Center opens. The Cancer Center houses leading-edge technology such as Novalis radiosurgery platforms and positron emission tomography scanners.

2003

MARCH 13
Sioux Valley Hospitals and Health System demonstrates an early indication of what will become a pattern of partnering with other community entities with the announcement of an agreement between the health system and the local YMCA to build a large $8 million wellness center on Sioux Fall's west side.

Sanford Health board of trustees. "So the board's job is always to understand when to pull in the reins. To Kelby's credit, he put together an organization that either has the damndest work ethic that I ever saw, or they're just that smart that they don't make a lot of mistakes, because I would have guessed that a couple of balls would have dropped and they haven't."[18]

A believer in the inspirational capabilities that words possess, Krabbenhoft envisions concepts that are "transformative." He speaks of considering new relationships with organizations only after "being invited" to discuss an opportunity by the potential partner. The CEO devises catch-phrases, called "Kelb-Speak" by close associates,[19] and peppers the corporate dialogue with them regularly. Everyone in the organization is familiar with these analects and they willingly adopt the principles, practices, goals, and aspirations they represent.

The phrase "promises made, promises kept" is an example and is realized time and time again as projects are started and carried out as pledged by Krabbenhoft.

Perhaps the foremost corporate principle emphasized by Krabbenhoft is what Sanford Health Chief Human Resource Officer Evan Burkett calls "Kelby's values of family."[20]

"The word we use many times as an organization is that we are family-centered or family-focused," said Ed Weiland, president of the Sanford Health Network Sioux Falls Region. "We take care of each other first of all, and that positions us to do our job and achieve our goals and our strategies very well."[21]

Ed Weiland, president of Sanford Health Network Sioux Falls Region, lifts up Sanford Health as a values-based organization.

2004

MAY 23
Sioux Valley Hospitals and Health System is recognized by the *Argus Leader* for its "culture of excellence," in its "Best in the Business" section. Employee involvement and satisfaction are cited as the reasons why the system has effectively been "growing according to community needs [and] pursuing good patient care." The system is cited for its "service excellence initiative, which is not so much a program as a culture," and for its values, "which include trust, ownership, risk taking, caring, health, and spirit."

2005

SEPTEMBER 12
Krabbenhoft develops a $400 million transformational health care and research plan with national and global impact and obtains commitment for such a donation from Denny Sanford.

As a devoted husband and father who has three children with his wife Heidi, a nurse, Krabbenhoft firmly asserted, "Family comes first. Yes, we've got to take care of patients, and, yes, that's the priority that's always there, but if somebody is hurting—one member of our family's kids is hurting—that's got to be tended to. Take the afternoon; go deal with it. Because we've got 25,000 people, we can figure out how to cover for that four hours. We'll figure it out."[22]

The notion of family goes even further, said Krabbenhoft, who considers working in the health care field as a calling and sought to hire those with a similar mind-set. "We provide scholarships for our employees' children. We send the message home ... that 'we want your daughter, we want your son, working for Sanford Health.'"

"We've been recruiting to culture," Krabbenhoft said. The idea that Sanford Health employees and professionals should feel a special bond and connection to helping people who need it is "in our orientations every week," he said. "And I say it in my opening comments to all the new hires."[23]

Working in the health care field is a calling and Krabbenhoft actively seeks to hire those with a similar mind-set. The idea that Sanford Health's 25,000 employees and professionals should feel a special bond and connection to the communities and people they serve is reinforced with every new hire.

2007

FEBRUARY 3

The $400 million gift from Denny and plans for its use are announced by Krabbenhoft, culminating in the largest gift ever to a health care organization. He introduces the name change from Sioux Valley Hospitals and Health System to Sanford Health to recognize Denny's magnificent gift and charitable spirit.

2009

JANUARY 5

A *Milwaukee Journal Sentinel* story on Joe Krabbenhoft, 6-foot-6 star basketball player for the University of Wisconsin Badgers, credits Joe's father, Kelby, with instilling in him the interest and determination to play the game hard. His father taught him that the most important word in basketball is "finish," Joe told the reporter. "Finishing the play on a loose ball. Everything. In life, finish. The word 'finish' really got nailed in my brain as a young kid." Siblings Sarah and Louis also played college sports.

Rick Giesel is the president of
Sanford Health Network,
Fargo Region.

"As I work with my team, that's how we live," said Rick Giesel, president of Sanford Health Network Fargo Region. "We use that terminology. I expect people who work for me do the same thing, but it all starts with Kelby. I think he expects the people that work with him to share that thinking and to be loyal to the organization. In turn, he's loyal back."[24]

Krabbenhoft is also deeply loyal to his profession and to his community, serving in leadership roles in various industry and community initiatives, as well as mentoring students, encouraging them to adopt the highest standards in personal conduct, academic pursuits, and life achievement. His efforts have taken root at the core of the organization. "It's just a genuine caring that you feel in this organization, that is the atmosphere that it has created, the 'M.O.' that it has created," Denny observed.[25]

Krabbenhoft's drive to shape and improve the operations entrusted to him is a key personal characteristic, a need to "take what I was given and make more of it," Krabbenhoft said. "The management of Sanford Health will be a function of the expectation of service, transparency, and success. Leadership will present a welcoming approval to ideas and provide clear direction and hold accountability for ensuring that quality and clinical excellence are central to our decisions." He acknowledged that it can be tough at times for the people who work with him closely. "It's inexcusable to think that I cruised at any time during my career, so I haven't, and at times I've worn out everybody around me because of that." Yet, this perpetual motion has led Sanford Health to crossing "huge chasms that other health systems haven't in handling the issues we have to deal with today."[26]

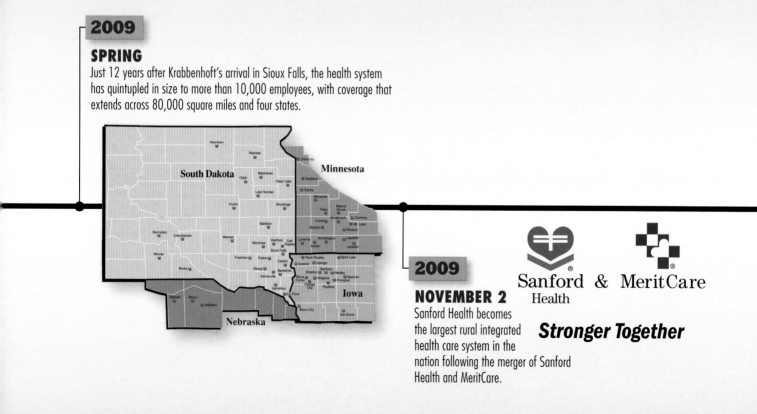

2009

SPRING
Just 12 years after Krabbenhoft's arrival in Sioux Falls, the health system has quintupled in size to more than 10,000 employees, with coverage that extends across 80,000 square miles and four states.

2009

NOVEMBER 2
Sanford Health becomes the largest rural integrated health care system in the nation following the merger of Sanford Health and MeritCare.

Sanford Health & MeritCare

Stronger Together

Everyone in the organization knows that Krabbenhoft envisions further growth and scale. He wants progress, and he wants Sanford Health to have a prominent place on the national and international stage and has established benchmarks for accomplishing it.

"There's always a new layer of value and of expectation that Kelby creates in order to make sure that none of us is satisfied with less than what should be satisfactory for a very high-caliber, high-standard organization," said Mortenson.[27] "The key we can't miss here in all of the things that our CEO talks about is the passion for health care and compassion for the patient," said Stork. "It's always in the forefront of his mind."[28]

Krabbenhoft (at right), entrusted as the principal custodian of The Gift, often finds himself alongside Denny making announcements of new initiatives and achievements.

2011

MARCH 1
Sanford Health completes a merger with North Country Health Services in Bemidji, Minnesota, integrating hospital and clinic and establishing Sanford Bemidji as a key regional hub in Northern Minnesota.

2012

JULY 2
Sanford Health completes a merger with Medcenter One in Bismarck, North Dakota. With the addition of Sanford Bismarck, the system reaches into seven states and extends coverage over 220,000 square miles, with 1,200 physicians, 25,000 employees, and facilities in 126 different communities.

CHAPTER FOUR

THE GIFT AND ITS IMPACT

I believe what you will hear and see today will be chronicled in books. Pay careful attention because history is being made, and you are a part of it.

—**Kelby Krabbenhoft**
Sanford Health CEO and president[1]

SIOUX VALLEY HOSPITALS AND HEALTH SYSTEM, BY 2005, WAS AN IMPRESSIVE enterprise with a great deal going for it. Many of the notions that Kelby Krabbenhoft brought with him, thoughts about what a successful health system should be and should accomplish, had been implemented by this time. While noteworthy, the portions of his vision that would lead to industry significance for the organization required magnificent and transformational philanthropy and would be the largest gift to a health care organization.

When Denny Sanford pledged The Gift of $400 million, it "really did accelerate everything that we were doing in ways that I don't think we even imagined at the time," said David Link.[2]

Much work and careful strategic planning took place between the time of the commitment on the part of Denny and the public announcement of The Gift more than a year later. A very small group of Sioux Valley Hospitals and Health System executives and trustees were able to keep this extraordinary secret. Both donor and recipient alike were committed to develop the platform for the programs The Gift would fund and ensure complete agreement on the principles. They were also determined to keep this monumental act of philanthropy under wraps, knowing that when the announcement was made, it would be so impactful that no one could doubt that this was a moment of transformation and that the future plans had been carefully strategized to make the best use of every dollar.

Opposite: The Washington Pavilion in Sioux Falls, South Dakota, was filled to capacity on the fiercely cold day in February 2007 when Denny Sanford's $400 million gift was announced.

Denny spoke about his desire to make a difference, particularly for children, on the day of the announcement as he explained why he had made such a huge contribution to this organization, one he was impressed with as being a great health care provider.

Confidentiality agreements were signed by the advertising and marketing staff who would be helping to publicize the initiative after it was announced. Board members swore themselves to secrecy, pledging not to mention it to anyone, not even their spouses. The board discussed development plans in confidential sessions, said Barbara Stork, who was vice chair of the board during the preannouncement process.[3] "We had some code words [and also referred to it as] Project 2011. ... It was absolutely amazing that the 40 people in that room kept that quiet for a year."[4]

The announcement of Denny's $400 million contribution took place at a gathering of employees; community, state, and federal leaders; and other stakeholders on a Saturday in February, the coldest day of that winter.[5] As about 2,000 people were gathered in downtown Sioux Falls' Washington Pavilion, just minutes away new signage heralding "Sanford Health," honoring the man with the generosity and heart behind all this, was being installed above the entrance to the hospital.

As the event unfolded before the excited audience, it was simulcast to

2007

FEBRUARY 3

Denny's transformational $400 million gift is made public, announcing five children's clinics throughout the US, research efforts, and The Sanford Project, an all-out effort to cure an as-yet-undetermined disease.

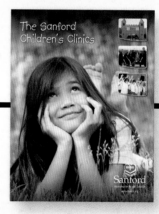

2005

SEPTEMBER 12

Kelby Krabbenhoft secures a commitment from Denny Sanford to donate $400 million to launch ambitious initiatives including curing a devastating disease and establishing clinics around the world. Since then, many exciting events and celebrations have recognized the progress and success of the entire Sanford Health organization.

Sanford Health employees throughout regional facilities who had to remain on premises caring for patients. To address the inevitable questions from employees, then Sioux Valley USD Medical Center President Becky Nelson returned to the institution to speak with the staff and celebrate the announcement.[6]

The media—local, regional, and national—heralded the gift for its astonishing size and for the significant programs it would set into motion. The Sioux Falls *Argus Leader* featured stories about the five new children's clinics to be built in various parts of the country and abroad "closely tied to the new Sanford Children's Hospital in Sioux Falls to expand its reach for this vulnerable population—a special interest of [Denny] Sanford."[7] The Sanford Project, focusing resources and attention on curing a disease in the near term, would be launched, and there would be a "campus of the future" approach that would take patient care and translational research to an entirely new level.[8] The $400 million would "help speed construction of new facilities on the Sanford Health campus with centers of excellence in treatment and research of cancer, childhood diseases, heart and cardiovascular

Becky Nelson returned to the hospital after The Gift announcement, working until after midnight to share the news and celebrate with staff members.

2007

FEBRUARY 17

Krabbenhoft says at a meeting with the *Argus Leader* newspaper editorial board that the previously announced five pediatric care clinics across the US and abroad have now grown into a much more ambitious 20 clinics around the world within a decade.

2007

FEBRUARY 4

Sanford Health puts out a request for proposals to invite applications for the Sanford Children's Clinic program.

diseases, orthopedics, and women's health ... and eventually, 20 separate specialized facilities will be joined in a world class medical center," the local newspaper also reported.[9]

The community realized that newly renamed Sanford Health was by no means the only one that would benefit from this significant gift. City and state leaders were almost immediately speaking of the huge economic impact the research project and other aspects of this growing organization would have on the area, just as Krabbenhoft and Denny had predicted. Sanford Health would recruit world-class talent to its new research park, and the positive leverage would be huge. An ecomomic impact study on The Gift reported $1.1 billion in new economic activity and 10,500 new jobs in 10 years as a result of The Gift.

"Silicon Valley was developed around a little chip. Why can't we do that [in Sioux Falls] with health care?" Krabbenhoft told an *Argus Leader* reporter. [10] The Gift would help transform the region into one of the most sophisticated centers for medical research in the country, raising standards of care throughout the region, possibly the nation, and helping to attract prominent researchers and top physicians. Philanthropic groups were hopeful that such a large gift would inspire others to take similar steps in their charitable giving.

Sanford Health set forth to help people understand that this was a gift to everyone. The theme for the communications included a blue bow symbolizing The Gift and the messaging described how it would benefit people and their health care throughout the region. The general public had immediately grabbed onto the new branding and understood why it was happening and thought it was a great thing.[11]

2008

APRIL 17
At a day-long meeting in Sioux Falls, champions of each of the four candidate maladies chosen as Sanford Project finalists by the consulting group hired by Sanford Health argue their cases. An advisory council that hears the presentations come to agreement on which one The Sanford Project should tackle: type 1 diabetes.

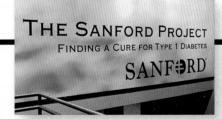

2007

JUNE
Sanford Health is selected as one of the original National Community Cancer Centers by the National Cancer Institute.

Denny's statements lift up his charitable spirit and interest in the fulfillment of the Sanford Initiatives.

A Balanced Approach

From the very beginning, Kelby Krabbenhoft had a well-defined strategy for allocating much of Denny Sanford's $400 million gift.

"Kelby did an amazing job of giving clarity to the fact that this wasn't some big slush fund to subsidize when we have a bad month as an organization," Brian Mortenson recalled,[1] but, rather, funding to support things that could not have happened otherwise.

For both internal and external audiences, "I think we did a really good job as an organization post-February 3, 2007, at identifying 'these are the Sanford initiatives, these are the very specific plans that this organization has to launch this new Sanford Health identity,' " said Mortenson.

It may have been somewhat easier to make this argument stick fast and permanently with this organization than it might have been with others because "such discipline" relating to financial sustainability permeated "every entity, every program, every hospital, and every component of the organization," that few assumed the $400 million was an overflowing barrel waiting to be tapped, Mortenson said.[2]

Across the organization, business would be conducted as usual, leadership continued to reiterate. This meant standards would be maintained and improved and fund-raising would continue for services that required contributions, with an ongoing focus on "dedication to the work of healing" now further enhanced by the opportunities associated with The Gift.

Right: Kelby Krabbenhoft, Becky Nelson, Denny Sanford, and Dr. Pat O'Brien at the May 2009 ribbon cutting for the Sanford Children's Hospital Castle of Care.

Below: Evan Burkett is the chief human resource officer for Sanford Health's entire community, spanning over 220,000 square miles.

Within Sanford Health, The Gift led to "an immediate increase in the number of people who wanted to be a part of Sanford Health because of job security, the promise of contributing to something quite amazing, [and] the belief that growth would be boundless, especially with the added new direction in research," said Evan Burkett, chief human resource officer.[12]

Of all the pieces highlighted that frigid February day, it was The Sanford Project that seemed to most captivate journalists and the greater medical community. The promise of curing some soon-to-be-announced disease in the foreseeable future was so appealing and compelling, it immediately grabbed and held headlines.

2009

MAY 15

Sanford Health accelerates research initiatives by purchasing the Hutchinson Technology Campus in Sioux Falls. Purchasing the 300,000-square-foot building allows Sanford Health to rapidly expand its multiple research initiatives, which have already seen significant growth in the past five years. The facility also serves as corporate offices in Sioux Falls.

2008

JULY 10

Todd and Linda Broin (top center) provided their $10 million gift to fund The Sanford Project chair position several weeks after the announcement that type 1 diabetes would be its focus. Having experienced long-term health issues caused by the disease in their own family, their gift also exemplifies how Denny's gift has inspired others. In Todd and Linda's words, "We came to the conclusion that in our lifetime we wanted to give a gift with a singular purpose that would improve people's lives."

Speculation about what disease would be tackled continued for months. Just about everyone had a recommendation or an opinion.

The media quoted scores of national experts who were certain it would be this disease or that. Sanford Health officials refused to be drawn into the discussion, telling reporters that they would take a considered approach to making the choice, relying on an independent panel of scientists to come up with options[13] based on a key stipulation: the disease was a pressing issue with national importance and there was sufficient evidence to indicate that a cure could be found within 15 years, during Denny's lifetime.

Sanford Health contracted with a nationally recognized medical research consultancy group, Battelle Technology Partnership Practice, to identify top contenders. "We need you to come in here, narrow the whole field of research," Krabbenhoft told them, "from toenails to hair follicles, and tell us what are the compelling maladies, diseases that are out there today that we can actually find a cure for. With money, with focus, with an unbridled, unbureaucratic environment, what disease type, what malady, what problem can we solve, can we actually deliver a cure for, like Pasteur did, like Salk did?"[14]

"We will supply this kind of funding. We want, obviously, to get researchers who can go and either bring their funding with them or access more funding from [the National Institutes of Health]," Krabbenhoft added. He would listen to everything they had to say, any suggestion, as long as they kept one thing firmly in mind: the time horizon for finding a cure was "nonnegotiable."

2009

SEPTEMBER
Renowned researcher Alex Rabinovitch begins The Sanford Project clinical trials, with the goal of finding a cure for type 1 diabetes. Dr. Rabinovitch's track record of chronic disease research spans decades.

2009

AUGUST 3
The first of the Sanford Children's Clinics opens in Duncan, Oklahoma. The 8,000-square-foot facility, with the same castle motif used for the Sanford Children's Hospital in Sioux Falls, provides pediatric care for children in the area, some of whom previously had to travel more than an hour to see a pediatrician.

Battelle launched a massive outreach effort, interviewing dozens of scientific leaders and researchers to come up with its provisional list of 14 illnesses: Alzheimer's disease, atrial fibrillation, cervical cancer, congenital heart disease, type 1 diabetes, heart failure, inflammatory bowel disease, lupus, multiple sclerosis, neonatal brain injury, Parkinson's disease, pediatric brain tumors, rheumatoid arthritis, and stroke.[15] Then, working with Sanford Health leaders and a council of national experts that Battelle had convened, a final-four list emerged of cervical cancer, type 1 diabetes, lupus, and multiple sclerosis.[16]

With a mandate focused on curing a disease, the Sanford Health board of trustees developed The Sanford Project, which set an ambitious goal to cure type 1 diabetes.

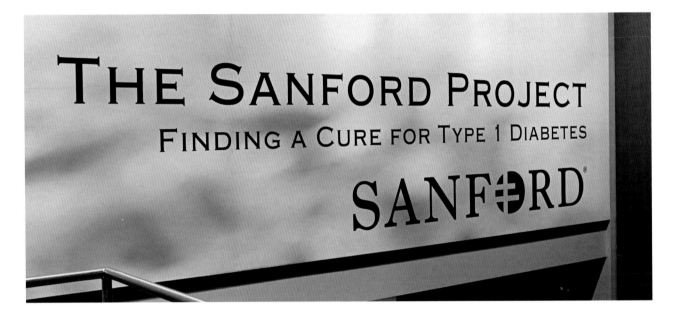

2009

SEPTEMBER 10
Sanford Health breaks ground on the new Sanford Heart Hospital in Sioux Falls.

2010

JUNE
The Sanford Research Center, home to Sanford Health's expansive research efforts, opens in Sioux Falls, in an ultramodern, state-of-the-art facility where dozens of researchers conduct their work.

From Sioux Falls to Worldwide

The idea for establishing clinics where special service opportunities and needs exist throughout the country and the world was born when Kelby Krabbenhoft and David Link were sorting out details of initiatives and ideas to present to Denny Sanford when Krabbenhoft was envisioning his discussion with Denny.

Link suggested a network of children's clinics, and "a lightbulb went off in my head," Krabbenhoft said. "It's something we do well. We put outreach clinics … in locations around our region all the time. Doing it in additional locations would not be so very different. We could even do a couple across the borders, if invited, in Mexico or Canada."

Krabbenhoft and Link quickly developed more ideas and plans that would make the clinics self-sustaining local start-up partnerships.

When the plan was announced in February 2007, Krabbenhoft said there would be five clinics, and possibly one would be in Mexico.

Within days of the announcement, the number Krabbenhoft was speaking of had quadrupled to 20, and the idea of expanding in a big way outside of North America had taken root.

"We put out the request for proposals and invited communities to let us know what their needs were, and the service and local partnership opportunities, and then two other staff members and I visited selected candidate communities," said Ruth Krystopolski, executive vice president for development and research,[1] who was overseeing the development of what now are referred to as World Clinics.

By 2012, clinics were operating or were being built at seven sites outside of Sanford Health's market: in Duncan, Oklahoma; Oceanside, California; multiple cities in Ghana, Africa; Klamath Falls, Oregon; Dublin, Ireland; Baja, Mexico; and Karmiel, Israel.[2] Several more sites were being contemplated.

Today, Sanford Health continues to move forward globally because "we have broadened our vision not only to being a regional hospital with a great reputation, but also to being one of the top hospitals in the nation, to even begin thinking about having a worldwide footprint," Ron Moquist of the Sanford board said.[3] The company expects to achieve its 20 clinics on schedule, and even exceed those numbers.

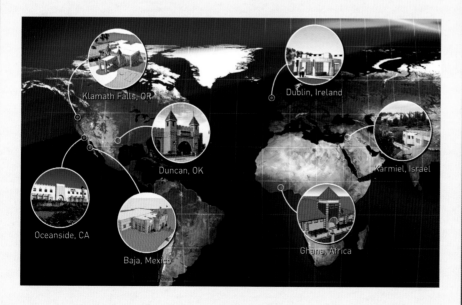

In Spring 2008, at a day-long meeting in Sioux Falls, arguments for the four final-ists were presented by a champion for each malady identified by Battelle. An advisory council heard the presentations and recommended the one that would receive among the most intense investigations and scrutiny ever launched: type 1 diabetes. The Sanford Health Board of Trustees approved this recommendation and The Sanford Project to cure type 1 diabetes commenced.

The reasons the council gave for making its choice included, "the regeneration focus [that was proposed] is cutting edge and gets at the root of the disease," there were "strong synergies with Sanford Children's Health Research Center," and it "offers a strong platform to grow future research programs at Sanford Health."

Krabbenhoft was thrilled to have a decision. Finally, the work could begin. "I don't profess to know the intricacies of the human genome or the connectivity between the chemical and the cellular level that will reveal in the pancreas a solution to beta cells that will solve type 1 diabetes. That's not my deal," he said years later. "I have the other part of the deal. I got to set up the organizations, facilities, and funding, and put it in the hands of people that will deliver."[17]

The Sanford Project start-up was greatly aided by a $10 million gift from Todd and Linda Broin to fund the chair (director) position for the project, enabling the recruit-ment of the best candidate. Six premier researchers and their teams of investigators were recruited and began their work.[18] In a matter of months, the project had elevated itself in laboratory circles to an enviable position. "From my years of being in this field, I know all

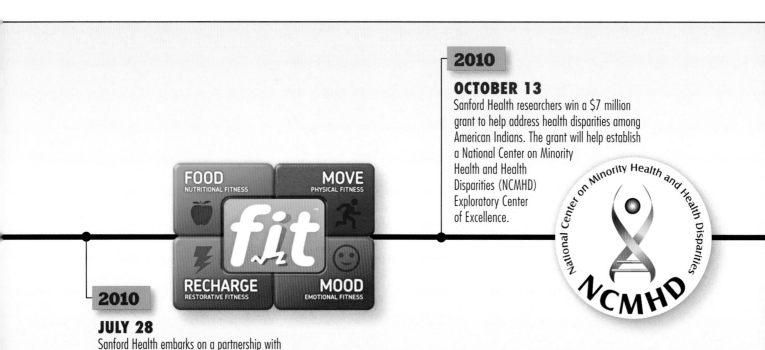

2010

OCTOBER 13
Sanford Health researchers win a $7 million grant to help address health disparities among American Indians. The grant will help establish a National Center on Minority Health and Health Disparities (NCMHD) Exploratory Center of Excellence.

2010

JULY 28
Sanford Health embarks on a partnership with WebMD and The Walt Disney Company to create "fit," an interactive online site to encourage a healthy and active lifestyle for children ages 2 to 18. Visit fit at http://fit.webmd.com.

Dr. Alex Rabinovitch, an internationally known researcher, heads up the team of researchers working on The Sanford Project to find a cure for type 1 diabetes, serving as the Todd and Linda Broin chair and director of The Sanford Project.

the players, in academia, in the funding agencies, and we talk to one another, and when I say, 'Sanford Project calling,' that opens the door because they know we're going to contribute to the cost," said Dr. Alex Rabinovitch, the Todd and Linda Broin chair and director of The Sanford Project.[19]

According to Krabbenhoft, "I get to provoke The Sanford Project scientists during our quarterly meetings, 'Where are we, guys? (Like the Pope asked Michelangelo about painting the Sistine Chapel). Is it done yet?'"[20]

The Importance of a Name

The name "Sanford" has a certain "elegance" about it, Sioux Valley Hospitals and Health System executives believed back when the $400 million donation and the concurrent name change were being discussed.

It is a happy coincidence that the contributor also happens to have a name that is easy to remember, that flows well off the tongue, and that looks good when it graces either correspondence or buildings, lending a certain cachet to an institution's branding effort.

The impact of a name is critical when an enterprise is aiming to extend its reach, secure recognition for innovation, and earn a place in the national spotlight.

Kelby Krabbenhoft knew that the regional link to a name difficult for people in other parts of the nation to spell would impede efforts to place the institution on the national stage. It was too provincial, too confusing, and would not be easily remembered.

So, soon after he began considering asking for the transformational donation, Krabbenhoft also began contemplating asking Denny Sanford to use his name. Beyond branding and the reach for a national audience, he wanted to honor the man himself.

"Denny was not seeking [his name in lights]. He never mentioned it," Krabbenhoft said. "I don't think he ever thought that what he was doing was about trying to make him as iconic as [Mayo or Johns Hopkins] but I did, and asked for his name to be put on our health system. It gave identity to our new resolve, our cause, and our culture."[1]

Once The Sanford Project was well under way, Denny contributes millions more to Sanford Health to launch the Edith Sanford Breast Cancer initiative, named for his mother who died of the disease.

There are regular reminders keeping everyone focused on the reason for working so hard: busloads of children with type 1 diabetes arrive with their parents three times a year to spend the day at the facility to meet the researchers and learn about the advances they are making in their research.

"I want to 'kill' this disease," Krabbenhoft said. "And I want Denny to stand on a stage someday and just proclaim: 'We did it. We got it done.'"[21]

As remarkable as the $400 million was, it did not turn out to be the last of the contributions Denny has made to his namesake health organization. His gifts continued in subsequent years, including an incredible $100 million contribution to launch the Edith Sanford Breast Cancer initiative.

Having lost his mother Edith to cancer when he was just 4 years old, he personally understood the pain that untold millions of families endure, and he wanted to help scientists understand and cure breast cancer.

Researcher Brian Leyland-Jones, MB BS, PhD, was chosen to lead the effort out of a special Sioux Falls facility focused on exploring a woman's entire genetic profile and looking for new ways to personalize treatment. The researchers aim to ascertain the fundamental

2011

MARCH 24
Sanford Health's second Sanford Children's Clinic opens in Oceanside, California, partnering with nearby Rady Children's Hospital to provide comprehensive, community-based care for the roughly 110,000 children that live within 10 miles of the facilities.

2011

AUGUST 17
The Edith Sanford Breast Cancer initiative, named after Denny's mother, is launched to conduct breast cancer research, foster a grassroots support network, and focus on personalized women's care.

question of why breast cancer develops, with the hope of developing better prevention and treatment approaches.[22]

"Breast cancer [research] is literally undergoing a transformation as we speak," Dr. Leyland-Jones said. He was willing to make the move to Sioux Falls because "It is extremely difficult to find the funds" to pursue this research effort, and "Kelby and Denny are committed to the vision. ... This gift has made it possible."[23]

Believing that genomics—the science of understanding the sequence and structure of genes—is key to coming up with a cure, part of the effort will entail collecting genetic

In making the announcement of the breast cancer initiative, Denny and Krabbenhoft are joined by national spokesperson Mary Hart, who has a family history of breast cancer.

samples from volunteers to create a biobank that may explain why two people respond so differently to the same cancer treatments. That discovery will be an important addition to personalizing breast cancer therapies.[24]

South Dakota native and longtime *Entertainment Tonight* television host Mary Hart, whose mother is a breast cancer survivor and whose grandmother died of breast cancer, was announced as the national spokesperson for the initiative in 2011.

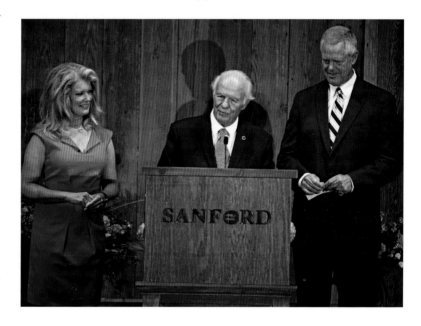

2011

AUGUST 20
Sanford Health announces that three new world clinics will be constructed in Cape Coast, Ghana; Karmiel, Israel; and Baja, Mexico.

PHOTO: © SUSAN LEGGETT/123RF.COM

2011

SEPTEMBER 15
Sanford Health partners with the American College of Sports Medicine to create the National Youth Sports Health & Safety Institute, which will advocate for developing and advancing research, education, and policy to enhance the health and safety of children and teens involved in sports and physical activity.

Denny pursues this issue with special vehemence. In a video on the Edith Sanford Breast Cancer Foundation website, he called it a "vicious disease" and made a moving plea to "halt this devastating disease," concluding with "please help me in saving mothers for children."[25]

In conjunction with the establishment of the Edith Sanford Breast Cancer program and the lead gift by Denny, the Edith Sanford Breast Cancer Foundation was initiated with a national grassroots effort to provide perpetual support, and a leadership team was brought on for the ongoing campaign, including President Kimberly Simpson Earle.

The efforts do not stop with diabetes and breast cancer. Sanford Research had been engaged in scientific research in the years before The Gift, but with its arrival, those efforts were increased with a new scope and intensity. By 2012, laboratories focusing on cancer biology, cardiovascular issues, children's health, type 1 diabetes, breast cancer, and health outcomes were working hard to find answers, and Sanford Health researchers are conducting dozens of research projects and many clinical trials in new treatments and devices.

"We developed a biobank and will invite every patient cared for in the health system to be part of it and our registry of DNA samples," said Dr. Eugene Hoyme, president of Sanford Research. The thinking is that "if we have an investigator who wants to look at genetic markers that predispose to high blood pressure, or if we have a sports medicine person who wants to look at the markers that predispose to injury, we would have the infrastructure here with hundreds of thousands of samples that we would be able to provide for them to use in their studies."[26]

Opposite: By 2012, Sanford Research has a large staff of researchers, all working to find cures and new treatments for some of the conditions and diseases that impact human lives.

Below: Dr. Eugene Hoyme, president of Sanford Research, insists that, instead of research for research's sake, the focus of research must be on improving the quality of patient care.

2012

JANUARY
Sanford Health announces that not only is the Ghana World Clinic now operational, a minimum of three more will be opened in that country before year's end.

CoRDS Registry
Coordination of Rare Diseases at Sanford

2012

MARCH 8
Sanford Research's CoRDS program (Coordination of Rare Diseases at Sanford) has been selected to join the International Rare Diseases Research Consortium (IRDiRC), an international group formed to work together across the globe to speed up research in the areas of rare disease. The CoRDS program was selected because of the work being done and the financial commitment to rare disease research.

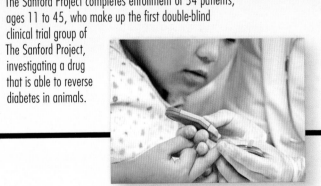

2012

MAY

The Sanford Project completes enrollment of 54 patients, ages 11 to 45, who make up the first double-blind clinical trial group of The Sanford Project, investigating a drug that is able to reverse diabetes in animals.

2012

JULY 28

Sanford Health implements electronic medical records (EMR) software in its Ghana clinics. EMR software greatly increases the efficiency and quality of patient care, but is often unavailable or severely limited in developing countries.

From "Computer Pro" to Senior Health Executive

David C. Link (above, on the right), senior executive vice president of Sanford Health, has played a critical role since 1990 in the growth and diversification of Sioux Valley Hospital and Sanford Health and has a "go-to person" relationship with Kelby Krabbenhoft and a close association with Denny Sanford.

Focused and articulate, involved in every major initiative, including helping Krabbenhoft formulate the plans he would present to Denny in 2005, and envisioning the concept of creating children's clinics around the country and around the globe, Link is a respected leader.

A former computer professional, Link had not pictured a career in health care when he entered the labor force three decades ago. He had the wisdom, however, to see and seize opportunity and to seek further education to follow a course of continued professional growth and development.

In the early 1980s, Link was running a small computer contracting business, and among his clients was Sioux Valley Hospital, which he had walked past every day on his way to school.[1]

"[For the hospital,] we were writing different inventory control systems, payroll systems, time and attendance, and all the things that become backroom activities of the organization," he said. "After about two years of that, Sioux Valley Hospital became probably 70 percent of my business. I had a few other clients, but [Sioux Valley Hospital] projects grew to consume most of my time."[2]

In 1983, Sioux Valley Hospital offered Link a position as director of data processing, a role he stayed in for six years while pursuing part-time his master's degree in business administration. With his new degree in hand, the human resources director suggested Link apply for a graduate-level fellowship to study health care administration, and he was granted a sabbatical when his request was accepted.

Fresh from the fellowship, Link became vice president of planning in 1990. "It was the first time we had a planning role in the organization," he recalled, and it was his responsibility to establish ways to infuse concepts of forward-thinking, vision, and strategy into the decision-making processes, working with others to develop "what the future of the organization should be like."[3]

Soon after Krabbenhoft's arrival, Link was promoted to executive vice president, in charge of physician practices to launch a new system health plan, then to senior executive vice president with special concentration on strategy.

It is not just research for research's sake. It is translational research. Everything "will then lead back to a program to take better care of our patients," said Hoyme. "The nice thing about having our research program being part of the health system is that all the research we do is focused toward patient care, ultimately translating to the patient's bedside ... focused on improving their health care."[27]

The scientific and personnel infrastructure is still growing, and the annual research budget is now $30 million. "Our goal is a hundred million dollars in research funding in this decade," said Hoyme. "I think we're likely to be able to make that goal."[28]

A key impact of The Gift, as described by Link, is that within hours of the gift announcement, an all-things-are-possible attitude took hold throughout the Sanford Health system.

"One of Denny's greatest gifts to the organization, far beyond the money—and the money is incredibly important—but far beyond that," said Link, "is the attitude of each and every leader in the organization that we can accomplish what we set our minds to, and it's that sense of hope and optimism that really pervades us. We have all sorts of problems and challenges and difficult debates, and we have budget realities and capital constraints like everybody else, but we have an attitude that ... 'it's up to us here.' We have the responsibility to do this. We all take that very seriously. It is our responsibility to, whatever the environment is, accomplish the things that are important for our patients."[29]

2012

AUGUST 1
Sanford Project researchers reach a critical milestone in a clinical trial testing a combination of two medications to determine if the drugs can help patients with type 1 diabetes keep their blood glucose levels under control with less or no insulin.

2012

OCTOBER 1
The Castle of Care Sanford Children's Clinic opens in Klamath Falls, Oregon.

2012

AUGUST 21
Sanford Health is awarded a $1.6 million grant to study and combat the unusually high incidence of cervical cancer in American Indian women. The five-year grant will fund research headed up by Subhash Chauhan, PhD, leading a team of seven researchers.

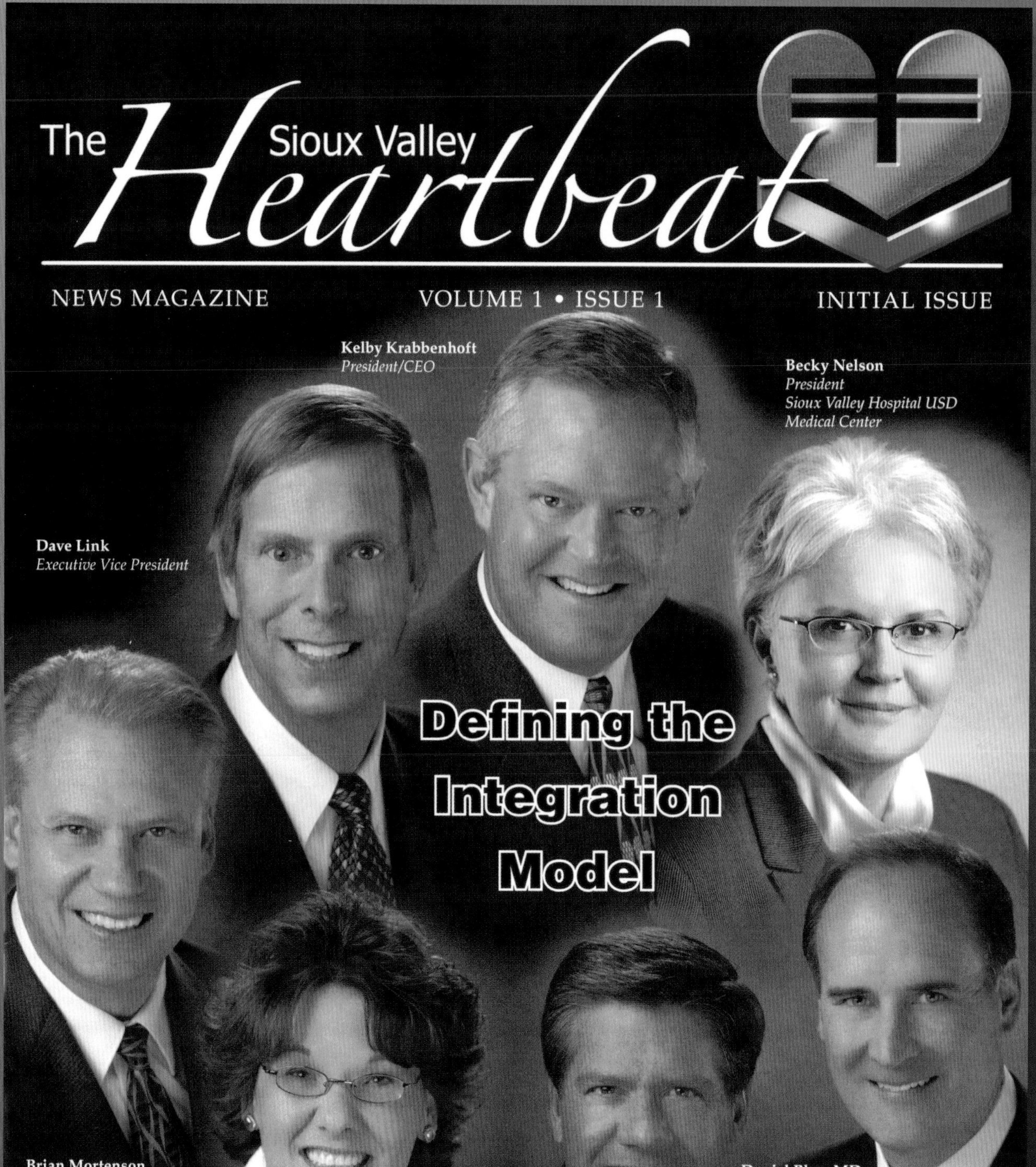

The *Sioux Valley* Heartbeat

NEWS MAGAZINE   VOLUME 1 • ISSUE 1   INITIAL ISSUE

Kelby Krabbenhoft
President/CEO

Becky Nelson
President
Sioux Valley Hospital USD
Medical Center

Dave Link
Executive Vice President

Defining the Integration Model

Brian Mortenson
President
Sioux Valley Foundation

Daniel Blue, MD
President
Sioux Valley Clinic

Ruth Krystopolski
Vice President
Managed Care

Ed Weiland
President
Sioux Valley Regional
Health Services

Dedicated To The Work of Healing

CHAPTER FIVE

HISTORY OF SIOUX VALLEY HEALTH SYSTEM

I am very proud of the fact that over the years at Sioux Valley Hospital, we never lost sight of why we were here and who we were here for—the patient, and we served to benefit the community.

—**Lyle E. Schroeder**
Sioux Valley Hospital Administrator,
President and CEO
1961–1996[1]

THE $400 MILLION GIFT TO SIOUX VALLEY HOSPITALS AND HEALTH SYSTEM and its transformational effect were built on more than a century of service to the area and a commitment to providing outstanding care for patients. The hospital had grown from a small facility to a full-fledged health system and had differentiated itself as a major medical center compared to the community hospital it was in the 1950s.

"Sioux Valley [Hospital] back then was basically like every other hospital in the state of South Dakota, only it was a little bigger," said Lyle Schroeder, who joined the hospital in 1953 as a part-time employee while in college. "We delivered babies. We did gallbladder surgery, appendectomies, and those kinds of things. So did the other small hospitals in the state of South Dakota. There wasn't a great deal of difference."[2]

That would not last long. During Schroeder's tenure as CEO, the hospital put the underpinnings in place that allowed Sioux Valley Hospital to grow first into a regional powerhouse, and then a national player.

Meeting the Community's Needs

In 1894, just five years after South Dakota had become a state, community and physician leaders of Sioux Falls decided they needed a hospital to serve the city's 7,000 residents.[3] This followed a visit to the Chicago World's Fair in 1893 where they experienced the marvelous

Opposite: When Sioux Valley Hospital initiated its magazine in 2005, *The Sioux Valley Heartbeat*, it had the pieces of integrated care in place.

tales of progress in medicine and the importance of the type of nursing care provided. It was to be a true community residents' hospital, with its $10,000 start-up cost covered by $10 shares purchased by local citizens. A few years after its incorporation, "Lutheran" was added to the hospital's name, reflecting the heritage of its founders.

As recounted in the *Sioux Valley Hospital School of Nursing Alumni Book 1898–1986*:

During its first 30 years of existence, Sioux Falls Hospital advanced through a rigorous course and developed its reputation for dedicated patient care led by its nurses and physicians.

Lutheran minister Reverend A. O. Fonkalsrud (above) was hired on December 1, 1925. The centerpiece of his legacy is—even through the beginning of the Great Depression—raising the money for, supervising the construction of, and opening a new building for the hospital (right), which was completed in 1930 at 19TH Street and Euclid Avenue, on the periphery of Sioux Falls at the time.

1894

Sioux Falls Hospital opens its doors with Dr. Arne Zetlitz (right) and Dr. H. Hovde as physicians in charge. The $10,000 in capital funds is raised by selling shares at $10 each to citizens in Sioux Falls and surrounding communities. Physician leadership has been a hallmark of the organization. When its electronic medical records system was first implemented, it was called "DocZ" in honor of Dr. Zetlitz.

1900–1930

A new building is constructed at the intersection of 19TH Street and Minnesota Avenue, marking the first facility in South Dakota built with the sole purpose of serving as a hospital. It would add "Lutheran" to its name, though it received no formal financial support from the Lutheran Church itself. A three-story expansion in 1915 sent the facility deeply into debt. Originally called Sioux Falls Hospital, it was renamed Sioux Valley Hospital in 1926.

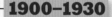

1899

OCTOBER

The Sioux Falls Training School for Nurses opens; Gena Stevens is the first of its three students and the only one to graduate in the inaugural class. Though the school was organized independently of the hospital, the two entities merged 20 years later when the school's original incorporation expired. The original group of alumni from 1900–1931 is called the "Gertrudes," in honor of a historical nursing student known for her maturity and dedication.

In the words of Ann Berdahl, RN, who served as hospital superintendent from 1922–1924
and later for 17 years as nursing education director—"The progress of civilization is
marked by the manner in which it cares for its old, its very young, its underprivileged, and
its sick and injured."

Lutheran minister Reverend A. O. Fonkalsrud, who had been a leader in developing St. Luke's Hospital in Fargo, North Dakota, was hired as administrator on December 1, 1925. One of the first changes he made was to gain agreement of the board of trustees, and in February 1926, the board decided to drop "Lutheran" from the name, to reflect the hospital's dedication to the entire Sioux Falls community. Fonkalsrud immediately began raising funds for a new building under the campaign theme "An institution of organized kindness"—with a goal of $300,000. No matter what name appeared on its building, however, patients and visitors found an abiding commitment to serving the community, the concept of compassionate care, and a commitment to excellence. With those principles serving as guideposts, the hospital grew and flourished, decade after decade.

In 1927, the actual building planning was under way for a new Sioux Valley Hospital. In February 1929, land was purchased and the next month construction began. Slowed by the Great Depression, the new building was finally finished in 1930. His feat accomplished, Fonkalsrud resigned in September 1931, handing the reins over to the Reverend C. M. "Cap" Austin. Austin put into place several debt reduction measures and instituted a cost-cutting

1943

During World War II, the Sioux Valley Hospital School of Nursing meets the standards for Cadet Corps training. In the Cadet Corps, nursing students were given financial assistance for training in exchange for service in the armed forces after graduation. Enrollment swells to 185 students from the previous 100. The hospital's nursing school closes in 1985 when clinical training affiliations with collegiate programs became the model.

1930

JULY 11

A new Sioux Valley Hospital facility is opened, with all patients transferring to the new building. The very next day, Spencer Valere Hollis (SVH) Brende became the first baby born in the new hospital, named by the nursing staff so that Spencer's name matched the initials of the hospital. The hospital is widely recognized for its obstetrics services and offers the latest advances in maternal child care.

regime to weather the depression that was ravaging the country, and indeed the entire world. As told in *I Remember—Sioux Valley Hospital School of Nursing Memories* by Leora Magestad Allen:

> *Hospital survival was also attributable to stalwart nursing supervisors and staff who at times worked for room and board and a stipend for necessities.*

Sioux Valley Hospital played its part during World War II, training nurses for service and treating soldiers from a nearby military base. The hospital responded to the polio epidemic after the war, with 400 stricken patients treated there in 1948 alone. The hospital, physicians, and staff developed an extensive program and facilities for polio patients and special services for children stricken with the disease, which would become the Children's Care Hospital and School.

When Schroeder was named administrator, he was the first in the hospital's history to have earned a master's degree in hospital administration. He began his tenure after a stable 1950s decade when the hospital's core function was still confined to general medical-surgical care and obstetrics.

With a new leader in place, Sioux Valley Hospital was ready to build its regional presence. In the words of longtime Sioux Valley Hospital board member Garry Jacobson, "Lyle always looked forward and put in place medical specialties—whatever was done was about how to serve the patient better."

Lyle Schroeder, longtime CEO of Sioux Valley Hospital, laid the foundation for what would become Sanford Health.

1944

Sioux Valley Hospital incorporates a school for children hospitalized for polio treatment. The program is under the supervision of the Sioux Falls public school system. A number of the local children unable to attend public school because of physical limitations are also enrolled.

1944

The federal government provides funds for a new wing, which expands the hospital to 190 beds. The hospital also cares for ill and wounded soldiers while a nearby military facility is under construction.

In 2007, Sioux Valley Hospitals and Health System became Sanford Health, and characteristic blue lights were added to campus facilities, recognizing The Gift from Denny Sanford.

Establishing Regional Strengths

Throughout the 1970s, Sioux Valley Hospital expanded its role in filling critical gaps in specialty care that existed throughout the region. When a national study showed that South Dakota had the third-highest infant mortality rate in the country, Sioux Valley Hospital launched its Neonatal Intensive Care Unit and the Perinatal Transport Service to carry sick newborns to its facilities. The first service of its kind in the Dakotas, it would later expand to serve adults, and be renamed "Intensive Air." The result was reduction in infant mortality to the second-lowest in the nation.

1961

Lyle Schroeder is promoted to hospital administrator, the first in the state to possess a master's degree in hospital administration. Known for his commitment to patients and the community, and his keen business sense, Schroeder became a recognized leader in the health care industry serving on several national boards.

1948

During the polio epidemic, the hospital's second floor is turned into an orthopedic and respiratory unit. As many as 20 tank respirators that helped polio patients breathe, commonly known as iron lung machines, are in operation. During the year, approximately 400 polio patients are admitted, taking precedence over all of the hospital's other services except emergencies and critical care. The organization has always responded in times of crisis.

Sioux Valley Hospital also developed a strong cardiology program, which drew in patients from across the region and further expanded its portfolio of specialties, including oncology, women's health, and orthopedics and sports medicine. By the early 1990s, Sioux Valley Hospital had grown to a 476-bed medical center with nearly 3,000 support and professional staff, serving close to 20,000 inpatients a year.[4] In 1985, it began formally providing outreach services to a network of rural facilities in four states, with 24 of them eventually becoming part of the Sioux Valley Health System through various lease and management agreements over the next 15 years.

During Schroeder's administration, the hospital took the first steps toward integrated health care, creating the Sioux Valley Physician Alliance in 1994. In its first year, the alliance had 40 doctors.[5]

The world of health care was changing; small community-based hospitals were finding it difficult to survive. Many were selling out to large, publicly traded hospital systems with deep pockets and distant headquarters.

"We had a successful hospital; we could have just stayed and been a hospital and kept our head down and what was the threat?" said Tom Everist, former board chair. "The world was changing. The nation's health system seemed broken. It was a cottage industry. Somebody needed to integrate it. If it wasn't going to be us, it was going to be somebody else. The argument was: 'We should do it, and we're big enough to do it, and it's worth doing, and it's worth controlling it here in our community, rather than letting some other model come from the outside.'"[6]

Tom Everist was the vice chair of the Sioux Valley Hospital board when they made the decision to hire Kelby Krabbenhoft.

1972

Schroeder examines the physician roster, including gaps and patient load, and concludes that the hospital needs to add a minimum of 40 physicians over the next two decades to keep up with growth in demand. The survey also shows the need for a neurologist. These forecasts and goals are a vital step in Sioux Valley Hospital becoming a regional medical center.

1962

Construction begins on a new west wing, which would initially add three new floors. The structure is built in such a way as to allow three additional floors to be constructed in the future. The need certainly existed in 1961, when the hospital operated at 90.7 percent capacity.

Sioux Valley Hospital's system development and network programs could now be established and executed to provide a foundation for integration. Together with a strong balance sheet, Sioux Valley had the confidence—and the funding—to expand.

"If you looked around at the best organizations in the country at the time, they were really all fully integrated organizations," said Dave Link, vice president of planning in 1990

Selected as Lyle Schroeder's replacement, Kelby Krabbenhoft grew Sioux Valley Hospital into Sanford Health, a regional health care powerhouse with a global presence.

New Research Emphasis

When Kelby Krabbenhoft arrived at Sioux Valley Hospital, he realized that even though clinical research was being done, there was not enough attention being paid to translational research, taking the results of basic research to benefit patients.

The hospital committed $1 million a year for a 10-year period to create a research partnership with the University of South Dakota. That partnership would begin to fill in that gap, and would also lay important groundwork for what would become Sanford Research and other research initiatives such as The Sanford Project in the coming years. Sioux Valley

Hospital began to develop the knowledge, understanding, and relationships that would later prove vital to securing and capitalizing on The Gift.

With the announcement of the $400 million donation by philanthropist Denny Sanford, researchers around the world took notice; resumes and grant applications began to pour in. "It's the perception, and people can see the potential, too," said Evan Burkett, chief human resource officer. "We love people who want to come back to the area. We know we're going to have those people for a long time."[1]

1977

South Dakota has the third-highest infant mortality rate in the country. Sioux Valley Hospital responds by offering the region's first air ambulance, the Perinatal Transport Service. The program is one of several coordinated efforts to combat the problem; Sioux Valley Hospital also helps train nurse practitioners and clinicians in neonatal care and has established expanded neonatal intensive care services.

1973

An $11 million expansion opens, adding 87 beds to the hospital. A clinic on Euclid Avenue is converted into an education center, providing classroom space for students from the various educational programs at the hospital.

Dan Kirby is past chair
of the board of trustees for
Sioux Valley Hospital.

and current senior executive vice president. "We needed to have all the pieces of the puzzle together—physicians, hospital, and the health plan—the financing aspect—if we were really going to do our best. We believed it was the best way to deliver care."[7]

A New Leader in Place

In 1996, Schroeder would retire after 36 years as head of Sioux Valley Hospital. As the board sought his replacement, it kept one key attribute at the top of its wish list: someone with a vision for integrated care.

"We knew we needed it," said Dan Kirby, board chair during the search for Schroeder's replacement. "We had learned enough about the industry to know that's what we needed. Our objective was to get to an integrated health care delivery system that could still be physician driven, and it still is, but the community had to own it. We thought of this as a community asset."[8]

"We were going to be a system, but we needed somebody to make this a system," stated past board member Tom Everist. To Kirby and Everist, Kelby Krabbenhoft stood out for his experience with an integrated care model in Joplin, Missouri, and for his strong vision, and the board selected him as the new CEO.

Kirby and Everist were right: Krabbenhoft had big plans, and they centered firmly on Sioux Valley Hospital's development of an integrated model of health care delivery.

1978

Sioux Valley Hospital opens its Same Day Surgery unit. Four years later, it devotes an entire floor to outpatient surgeries and procedures. This means significant cost savings and greater convenience for patients. The new floor operates autonomously, with its own waiting rooms, operating rooms, and staff.

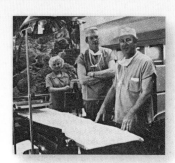

1980

Realizing the importance of lifestyle in health care, Sioux Valley Hospital converts its education center into a Wellness Center. The new center helps those who want to take charge of their health by offering education and exercise programs.

Another Piece of the Puzzle

In 1997, Sioux Valley Hospital reorganized under the name Sioux Valley Hospitals and Health System. A health plan was now key to Sioux Valley Hospitals and Health System's move to an integrated model. The issue had been contemplated for some time, even before Krabbenhoft came aboard.

After he arrived, the idea was again discussed during a board retreat; Krabbenhoft firmly committed. Once at the helm, he and Link wasted no time in starting to develop the health plan.

Ruth Krystopolski, who was running a health plan in Kalispell, Montana, was one of the first people called by Krabbenhoft, who with his typical sense of urgency, took the direct approach. "So I called him back, and then came and interviewed, and then actually moved here about 90 days after that," she said.[9]

Everything else about the health plan moved just as quickly. In nine months, Krystopolski hired staff, received licensing in the four states in which Sioux Valley Hospitals and Health System then operated, and developed systems and processes from the ground up. "Somehow we got it all done," she said.[10]

By January 1998, the health plan was up and running, quickly enrolling all of Sioux Valley Hospitals and Health System's own approximately 7,000 employees, and working through independent insurance agents to spread the word.[11] The first commercial plan was sold three months later, on April 1, 1998. Sioux Falls Christian School became the very first outside client and continues with the plan to this day.[12]

Ruth Krystopolski designed, launched, and now runs what is today known as Sanford Health Plan, a key component of Sanford Health's integrated medicine model. She serves as executive vice president of development and research, and Sanford Health Plan president.

1982

The Perinatal Transport Service expands to carry adult trauma victims in addition to pediatric patients. It is renamed "Intensive Air." The two airplanes—a Cessna 401 and a Beechcraft King Air—are equipped with heart monitors, defibrillators, and respirators. A sophisticated ground-to-air communications system allows for communication between the aircraft and the hospital from anywhere in the United States. The Intensive Air fleet will grow to also include helicopter service.

1990

Sioux Valley Hospital opens the new Heart Center, which includes an intensive care unit, surgical suites, a coronary care unit, rehabilitation services, and office space for cardiologists practicing at the hospital.

Over the years, under the Lorraine cross, Sioux Valley Hospital (now Sanford USD Medical Center) has been a beacon of healing and hope for residents of Sioux Falls and the surrounding region. Today it stands as one of the finest medical centers in the country, providing specialized health care, research, and education and serving as the primary teaching institution for the Sanford School of Medicine–University of South Dakota.

"Our readiness for the future was forged from a commitment to excellence in hospital and nursing services and built on innovative and dedicated medical leadership," stated Becky Nelson, chief operating officer of Sanford Health, in the 2004 Annual Report.

1991

Specially designed to provide care for the terminally ill, South Dakota's first hospice facility opens its doors. The Sioux Valley Hospice Cottage provides four bedrooms in a homelike atmosphere.

1992

Sioux Valley Hospital focuses services for specific populations. The Breast Health Institute is formed as a center for women's health information. It includes a low-dose mammography unit to screen for breast cancer. The Geriatric Health Institute also opens, offering clinical evaluations and treatment plans for the elderly population.

By 2012, 82,000 people were subscribers, and the health plan had a steady growth trajectory of 10 to 14 percent per year.[13] Much of the success is attributed to the health plan having a keen awareness of the needs of the local region and maintaining a close relationship with the employers and plan members it serves. The organization sets up a work-site wellness program for employers, and for some, it places a nurse practitioner on-site to serve wellness goals and other health interests.

When launching the health plan, Sioux Valley Hospitals and Health System opted to follow its own path. That meant two key differences from its health plan competitors: it would work with independent agents rather than its own sales team, and it would not spend heavily on marketing, choosing rather to place its emphasis on customer service. Link said:

Home to Five Centers of Excellence

Envisioned in 1999 by Kelby Krabbenhoft and Becky Nelson, Sanford Health's pursuit of excellence in patient care has been led by five Centers of Excellence—heart care, cancer, children's care, women's health, and ortho/neuro/trauma, which enhance the organization's reputation on its quest to maintain the highest standards.

"We define our market leadership in the five sentinel Centers of Excellence that we cornerstone our behavior around," said Krabbenhoft.

Sanford Health has a goal of leadership in every measure of performance. Krabbenhoft explained, "It's a lofty, very difficult, significant goal. Those things define our accomplishments. Best-in-business performance is about what the staff in our system does."[1]

1993–1994

Sioux Valley Hospital begins to receive acclaim as one of the country's top hospitals. In 1993 and 1994 it is named to the Top 100 Hospitals in America according to an HCIA survey, one of 25 hospitals to make the list in two successive years. In 1996, it is ranked as the region's best-performing hospital in *U.S. News & World Report*'s list of "America's Best Hospitals."

TOP **100** HOSPITALS IN AMERICA

1994

In its centennial year, Sioux Valley Hospital grows to become a 476-bed medical center with nearly 3,000 support and professional staff members, serving nearly 20,000 inpatients a year. It hosts a gala with TV personality Mary Hart, whose grandmother had been a Sioux Valley Hospital nurse, as keynote speaker.

This map shows Sanford Health's coverage and extensive locations of hospitals, clinics, and long-term care facilities prior to the merger with MeritCare.

We wanted to work with employers one-on-one and understand what their needs are. We had done market research early that showed that one of the bigger concerns of employers was customer service. So we made sure, from the start, that we built customer service that was best in class and we responded immediately to any type of questions or concerns that people would have. We provided reporting to the employers with a degree of detail that they were not used to. We then adopted a key philosophy. We said, "We're with you for the long term, and so we're going to give you a more predictable path of rate increases."

1996

Kelby Krabbenhoft is hired to replace retiring Lyle Schroeder, who had led the organization for 36 years. Krabbenhoft had served as president and CEO in Joplin, Missouri, prior to joining Sioux Valley Hospital. Before Krabbenhoft's appointment, the board had signaled plans to move toward integrated care, and selected Krabbenhoft for his experience with the integrated care model and his vision for carrying it out.

1994

Sioux Valley Physician Alliance starts up with 40 physicians representing primary care groups. Additional specialty practices and other physicians join over the next five years, growing the practice group to 120 physicians.

The health plan provided not only a key aspect of integrated care, but also helped keep the organization abreast of issues in the wider health care marketplace. "We learn so much from having a health plan," Link said. "We understand what the other payers are looking for and thinking of, but we also know our subscribers' health activities, not just what they're doing with us, but if they're doing things outside of the Sanford Health organization. We get a better view of the services that we may need to develop in the future."[14]

Dave Link serves as senior executive vice president of Sanford Health and is a key member of the leadership team, having helped guide the organization through many changes and tremendous growth.

Building Physician Practices

By the first part of the decade, Krabbenhoft had already begun building and shaping Sioux Valley Hospitals and Health System into a true integrated health system. After just a few years he had already doubled the system from $260 million in annual revenues to more than $500 million, and by this time the employee census exceeded 9,000. Sioux Valley Hospitals and Health System had taken important steps in developing its Sioux Valley Clinic model. In 2005, *The Sioux Valley Heartbeat* magazine noted that this included the addition of other specialty groups to the clinic and establishment of a physician board of governors. This board served as a structured and coordinated method for physician leadership and decision making in the system. Based on a strong foundation, growth of the Sioux Valley Clinic was moving forward. A significant event saw that effort escalate to a higher level. The purchase of Central Plains Clinic doubled the number of physicians in the organization. Central

1998

Sioux Valley Health Plan is launched. The first 7,000 members are all Sioux Valley Hospitals and Health System employees and family members. Three months later, the Sioux Falls Christian School becomes the first client.

1997

Sioux Valley Hospital changes its name to Sioux Valley Hospitals and Health System, better reflecting its broad-ranging services.

Sioux Valley
Hospitals & Health System

The merger with Central Plains Clinic and growth in Sioux Valley Clinic's physicians and locations helped Sioux Valley Hospitals and Health System reach its goal of becoming a fully integrated health system with the resources and reach to offer the highest level of health care to its patients.

Plains was struggling financially at the time, leaving the physician-owners in a precarious position. It already had facilities on a competing campus but would move to Sioux Valley Hospital's premises after the acquisition.

"I didn't feel like we were really prepared for the changes that were occurring in medicine, and so we struggled, troubled with how we could change so fast," said Dr. David Thomas, a pulmonary specialist formerly with Central Plains Clinic. "The merger with Sioux Valley [Hospitals was] a breath of fresh air for me. It gave us the opportunity to run our own practice and make our own decisions and yet still have the guidance and oversight from a business model that suited us well."[15]

2001

Sioux Valley Physician Group merges with Central Plains Clinic, adding about 120 specialty physicians to its team and almost 1,000 full- and part-time employees. The addition of the clinic helps Sioux Valley Hospitals and Health System reach its goal of becoming a fully integrated health system.

Everist recalled Krabbenhoft explaining the philosophy to doctors: "Kelby made it easily understood we wanted to merge the best aspects of private practice with the efficiencies and standards of a group setting." Still, it was not the hospital's style to demand that the clinic's physicians provide referrals to Sioux Valley Hospital. "Our approach was that, from day one, we were going to earn their referrals," said Everist.

Though the timing of the merger was precipitated by the clinic's financial difficulties, it was actually a natural match, said David Danielson, former administrator of Central Plains Clinic and now a Sanford Health executive: "When we were at the Central Plains Clinic board meeting with the Sioux Valley Hospital board, the Sioux Valley board espoused the same things that Kelby talked about, and you could see that they really deeply believed in that, and where their mission was, and where they were going. That's what made the difference."[16]

As Dr. Michael Farritor, Sanford Clinic chief operating officer, recalled, "Everything was about timing. We've never gone after someone who hasn't made an overture to us first. We don't go into a place and say 'you know, we'd really like to have you'—we just haven't had to do that. It's usually in reaction to a phone call or something. They say 'Well, we'd like you to look at us.'"

Dr. Mike Olson, former chair of the Sioux Valley Clinic Board of Governors and Sanford trustee, agreed, adding, "We both knew we needed each other. It's always been, 'How do we deliver better care to more people for less money? How do we give the best care?' Without that, it's not worth anything. You look at organizations like

Dr. Mike Olson is former chair of the Sioux Valley Clinic board of governors, which helped steer the merger with the Central Plains Clinic.

2003

Two major, multimillion dollar expansions occur. The NORTH Center provides space for orthopedic surgeons, neurologists, and neurosurgeons, among others. A $30 million center devoted to cancer treatment also opens.

2006

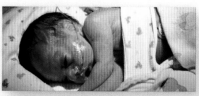

Expansions at the hospital include a $55 million surgical center that doubles the operating room area and quadruples the size of the recovery unit. The Boekelheide Neonatal Intensive Care Unit opens, featuring 47 private rooms and state-of-the-art lifesaving technology for the smallest of newborns.

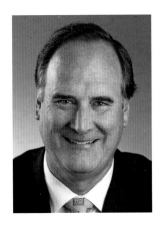

Above: Dr. Dan Blue is the president of Sanford Clinic.

Above right: Dr. Richard Hardie previously served on the Central Plains board and is currently a Sanford Health board member.

the Mayo Clinic—it's been there for a hundred years, or the Cleveland Clinic. How did they get there? The emphasis always has to be on cost-effective, efficient, state-of-the-art care."[17]

Sioux Valley Hospitals and Health System remained committed to building its physician organization while maintaining its community leadership. Though it was growing to an enterprise scale, it retained its community perspective and values. "We were a physician-driven, physician-integrated organization, and committed to the community," said Terry Baloun, past chair of the board of trustees for Sioux Valley Hospitals and Health System.[18]

With Central Plains Clinic now in the Sioux Valley organization, the health system continued its efforts to include more physician practices, joining with small- to medium-sized groups in all specialties. "Each one of them really was the cream of the crop," said Dr. Dan Blue, president of Sanford Clinic. "They were stand-out groups independently that always worked closely together and with this hospital, and had a great deal of respect for one another."[19]

According to Dr. Richard Hardie, a current Sanford Health board member, "The most important aspect about our discussions with Sioux Valley was our common interest in ensuring continuity and quality of care."

2007

Sioux Valley Hospitals and Health System was renamed Sanford Health to honor the generosity, great character, and spirit of philanthropist Denny Sanford. His $400 million gift will transform the organization and ignite exciting initiatives.

Sanford Health

2009

Sanford Health and MeritCare merge to form the new Sanford Health system, the nation's largest, rural, not-for-profit health care system with locations in 112 communities in seven states. This provides additional regional service opportunities and expansion of integrated medicine, health plan growth, and increased research and education.

SANFORD™ HEALTH

2009

By 2009, Sanford Health had expanded to 24 hospitals, 128 clinics, 38 long term care facilities, with 10,000 employees and 400 physicians serving a region of 80,000 square miles. The Sanford Children's Hospital opens, and the Sanford Initiatives are under way.

Gary Duncan, the CEO who replaced Krabbenhoft at the Freeman Health System, recounted in a March 2001 *Argus Leader* article:

He is a master at putting together a system and getting it poised for the future, and he's a warrior. He's not deterred easily. When he sets a vision, he's able to achieve it.

A Vision for Growth

The essence of Sanford Health's commitment to the integrated model and being a physician-driven organization is the "Covenant" established between the Sioux Valley Clinic physicians and the system in 2005. It articulated responsibilities of each around patients, leadership, communication, education, research, professional behavior, reward, and community service.

Sioux Valley Hospitals and Health System had established a significant position and role in regional medical care and multispecialty physician services. Its children's specialty services were growing, the cardiovascular program had been rebuilt following the exodus of a private cardiac group that started a physician-owned hospital, oncology care was becoming more sophisticated with new treatment equipment and drug therapies, women's health was a leading service in all respects, and orthopedics and sports medicine had grown in depth and relationships.

Clinical expansion was occurring throughout the region as a number of new clinics and hospital facilities were being added. The Centers of Excellence concept was in full force, and employee engagement and empowerment were being executed through a system-wide Service Excellence program focused on quality and professional development. The Sioux Valley Hospitals and Health System's continued development ensured rural hospitals, some with nursing homes and clinics, offered increased access to system health care services in their communities.

Each Center of Excellence had its own requirements and opportunities, but the catalyst of Denny Sanford's gift created a new momentum leading to a new pediatric residency program and participation in new research endeavors involving the National Cancer Institute and children's health and other specialized research.

After the receipt of Denny's gift, a new divisional structure was established. Headed by Dave Link, senior executive vice president, the Development and Research Division was designed to provide focus and leadership to the new Sanford Initiatives including Sanford Research, global clinics, and The Sanford Project. It also housed the health plan, foundation, and information technology. Sanford Health's clinical program development intensified in the Health Services Division, including the medical center, clinic, and network, under the leadership of Becky Nelson, senior vice president and chief operating officer.

As Sanford Health's transformation played out in national and global ways, a broader vision with regards to its regional service landscape was developing. This vision for growth was premised on the principles of trust and relevance to those served to ensure improvement in health care, research, and education.

MeritCare was an adjacent but regionally separate health system that had been on parallel tracks in its development of integrated health care and physician-driven character and had a shared community orientation with Sanford Health. Discussions between the leaders of the two organizations began in early 2009, which led to the next evolution of Sanford Health, exemplifying a common integration model and shared "Dakota values."

CHAPTER SIX

HISTORY OF MERITCARE HEALTH SYSTEM

Our founders were giants on whose shoulders we have stood to lead the way to the destiny that is now MeritCare. Dr. Olaf Sand and Dr. Nils Tronnes were the physician founders of St. Luke's Hospital and Fargo Clinic. They had the fire in their hearts. ... They lit a torch to show us the way. Because of that fire, we are here today. Their purpose from the beginning was to leave a light, and so they did, and so shall we.

—Dr. Roger Gilbertson
MeritCare CEO
1993–2009[1]

FARGO, NORTH DAKOTA, HAD A GREAT HEALTH CARE SUCCESS STORY IN MeritCare, an entity formed by the merger of a hospital and a clinic. The vision of growing to better serve the region exemplified the MeritCare spirit from its formation as St. Luke's Hospital and Fargo Clinic more than 100 years ago.

The Historical Foundation of Integrated Care

Lars Christianson emigrated to the United States and settled in Fargo, North Dakota, in 1881. A religious man, he strongly supported the charitable endeavor of taking care of the sick and injured. As a pharmacist, he had an acute awareness of the health needs of the fledgling city of Fargo, established just 10 years before.

Drs. Olaf Sand and Nils Tronnes worked out of a clinic above Christianson's drugstore in downtown Fargo. Day in and day out, they saw the need for improved health care in the community, so they called for a meeting of local leaders. After discussions and reaching a consensus regarding the need for a full-fledged hospital to serve the community, the group quickly settled upon a proposed site for the facility. Several locations were considered but ruled out due to the common 19TH century challenge of roads turning to mud and becoming impassable during inclement weather. Eventually a Broadway site was selected because of planned municipal

Opposite: Less than three years after the idea was discussed above Lars Christianson's drugstore, the new St. Luke's Hospital opened its doors in 1908.

developments in the area, and according to Dr. Tronnes, "It was easily accessible in all kinds of weather."

Shortly after a site had been selected, the organization began raising the needed funds by selling stock in the new hospital at $25 per share in a concerted effort to raise $50,000. Construction began in December 1906. In 1908, less than three years following that meeting above the drugstore, the hospital, complete with a school of nursing, opened its doors. A testament to the need for such a facility in Fargo, within three days the hospital was completely full with patients. By the next year, the hospital had to rent two residences to house additional staff, and by 1910, adjacent land was being purchased to make room for the growth that was so obviously needed. Meanwhile, due to poor crop harvests that year, solicitations from local farmers and businessmen were going slowly. It was Christianson who stepped up to the plate with an additional $10,000 over his previous investment, allowing St. Luke's to continue to move forward in a challenging economic climate.

The next year, in 1911, St. Luke's School of Nursing graduated its second class of seven nurses. Growing as rapidly as the hospital, the nursing school began plans in 1913 for a 20-room, two-story nursing student residence that also served to house patient overflow.

In 1916, Paul Vik, the hospital's administrator, announced plans to double the size of the hospital by constructing a new addition. To fund this growth, it again was Christianson who financed $60,000 of the hospital construction, adding 50 beds, three new operating rooms, kitchens, and an expanded boiler system.

1905

A meeting is held above Lars Christianson's drugstore in Fargo, North Dakota, to discuss the need for a Lutheran hospital in Fargo. Among those in attendance is Rev. A. O. Fonkalsrud, who later becomes administrator of Sioux Valley Hospital in South Dakota.

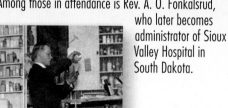

1908

The first three nursing students, Anna McDonald, Hazel Hodgson, and Olga Gronley, are in place at St. Luke's. Students receive 12 hours of classroom education each week, five months' training in the operating room, and three weeks in the laboratory.

1908

St. Luke's Hospital opens its doors in February and establishes the St. Luke's School of Nursing.

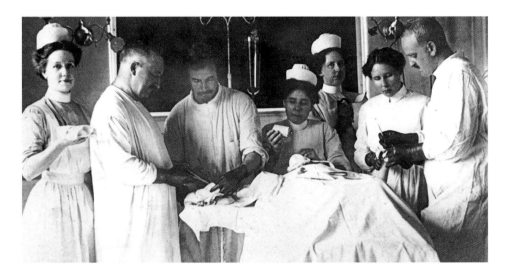

The surgical team at St. Luke's Hospital performing an operation in 1911. Pictured from left to right: Ms. Austin, Dr. Kachelmacher, Dr. Sand, Ms. Nordheim, Mrs. Bondahl, an unidentified nurse, and Dr. Tronnes.

The new expansion was just in time to allow the nursing school to train nurses to serve with the Red Cross during World War I, and also for St. Luke's to provide care for the victims of the worldwide Spanish-flu pandemic that raged from 1918 to 1919. The pandemic hit the Fargo community hard, with accounts indicating that one in three Fargo residents actually contracted the deadly sickness. St. Luke's surgeon Dr. O. J. Hagen wrote, "I had 1,300 flu-pneumonia patients scattered far and wide. ... I covered a 40-mile area surrounding Fargo and Moorhead."

Drs. Sand and Tronnes had both visited the Mayo Clinic in Rochester, Minnesota, and were both interested in applying the innovations they encountered there back in Fargo, albeit on a smaller scale. They spoke with the other doctors in town to determine the level of

1921

The Fargo Clinic, modeled after the Mayo Clinic, opens. Drs. Olaf Sand and Nils Tronnes, who had led the drive for the hospital, propose the specialty clinic where doctors work in a team setting.

OLAF SAND, MD

NILS TRONNES, MD

1909

Rev. A. O. Fonkalsrud is put in charge of the hospital's business affairs and plans the hospital's first expansion.

interest and support. Enough physicians agreed, and in April 1919, a group of the doctors presented the idea to the St. Luke's Hospital's board of trustees. Not only did the hospital board agree with the plans, but an agreement was reached for the hospital to supply heat to the clinic's adjacent building to be constructed, and for the clinic to provide laboratory services for the hospital. Later, the hospital purchased land previously sited for the clinic, and the newly formed medical group accepted 400 ownership shares in the Lutheran Hospital Association, the parent organization for St. Luke's Hospital. During the establishment of the Fargo Clinic, Dr. Sand was elected president, and St. Luke's administrator, Reverend A. O. Fonkalsrud, was named assistant secretary and treasurer. Thus began the hand-in-glove operational relationship between clinic and hospital, a relationship that would grow to exemplify the best in what is known today as integrated health care.

On May 2, 1921, the Fargo Clinic officially opened to the public. Dr. Sand stated in his inaugural speech at the grand opening gala words that still resonate today:

It has been said, and rightly so, that the most important person in a hospital or clinic is the patient. What advantages then can a clinic offer? The patient wants diagnosis and treatment. He wants it as accurate and efficient as possible, and at the least expense of time and money. In a clinic where all the means of modern science are brought to bear upon a given case and where a number of specialists cooperate, it would seem that the greatest possible accuracy and efficiency could be reached in the shortest possible time. ... There was a time when each doctor was self-sufficient, when

1939

North Dakota Hospital Association is formed, with St. Luke's Hospital as a charter member.

1923

St. Luke's Hospital serves a territory with a radius of 150 miles.

1939

Norway's Crown Prince Olav and Crown Princess Märtha visit St. Luke's Hospital on a trip to the United States. The two also visit Sioux Valley Hospital during that same US tour.

the same man was general practitioner, general surgeon, specialist in every line, and at the same time bookkeeper and collector. The individual doctor staggers under a burden of keeping in touch with all these branches of knowledge and the result is that he masters none. His financial resources fall short in the race with the ever-increasing number of diagnostic and therapeutic improvements. An X-ray machine, like an automobile of this year, may be out of date a year hence.

One way seems to be open cooperation through formation of groups where each man does the work he is most interested in and best fitted to do. Let all the diagnostic and therapeutic apparatus be common property. Group formation does not blot out, it liberates the personality of the doctor. It lifts him out of the rut and routine. The old saying that "a chain is as strong as its weakest link" does not apply to a group of doctors. The knowledge of the whole group is at the service of every member. There will be a leveling, but it will be a leveling up. The strength of the chain will be nearer that of its strongest link.

The clinic and the hospital continued to expand, introducing many new treatments and procedures to Fargo. The hospital opened an emergency room in October 1925, and in 1931 the hospital and clinic renegotiated their cooperation agreement, reaffirming and further strengthening the relationship. The Fargo Clinic promised to always provide adequate laboratory and X-ray facilities for St. Luke's Hospital, and the hospital promised not to add new services or capital equipment competing with the clinic. The clinic agreed not to add hospital beds, and the hospital agreed not to offer clinical services.

1940

St. Luke's Hospital joins with St. John's, Fargo's other hospital, to establish what would become Blue Shield of North Dakota. St. Luke's employees are covered under the plan with health insurance premiums of 65 cents per month.

1942

St. Luke's answers the nation's call by sending 10 doctors and more than a third of its staff to serve in the war effort.

Now in the midst of the Great Depression, St. Luke's Hospital ramped up charity efforts to both serve an economically devastated population and to shore up the hospital's finances. A year earlier a fund drive financed the bulk of a capital project, the construction of additional boiler and laundry capacity. To avoid layoffs, salaries of many employees were reduced. Christianson even restructured the outstanding debt the hospital owed him to ease cash flow.

By the end of the 1930s, the hospital, the clinic, and the economy were growing again. The nursing school had more applicants than available slots, and parking was now tight because more people had cars. The clinic began planning for a cancer center in 1939, launching a public health campaign to guide the public in cancer prevention.

In 1940, there was a positive atmosphere at the July board meeting as the hospital had built up a substantial cash balance, loans were being paid off, raises were once again being given, and a decision was made to increase the hospital nursing staff. In December of that year, a party was held celebrating the final payment of the loan Christianson had made to the hospital. Drs. Sand and Tronnes, signatories to the original loan agreement, personally signed the final check to Christianson, and a celebratory gala was held.

In 1942, the Fargo Clinic took the step of restructuring into a physician-owned clinic. Previously, the clinic had been owned by a group including the founding physicians, some family members, and outside investors. This move allowed doctors who had joined the clinic after its founding to participate in its ongoing growth and set the clinic up for long-term stability and success.

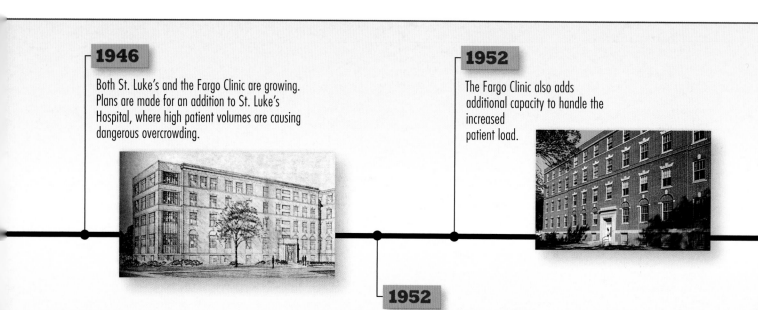

1946

Both St. Luke's and the Fargo Clinic are growing. Plans are made for an addition to St. Luke's Hospital, where high patient volumes are causing dangerous overcrowding.

1952

The Fargo Clinic also adds additional capacity to handle the increased patient load.

1952

Built with funds from a three-year fund-raising campaign, the four-story addition to St. Luke's opens.

When the US entered World War II, St. Luke's Hospital sent many of its physicians and their staff to aid in the war effort. By the war's second year, 10 doctors were away serving in the US Army, and 50 nursing school graduates were in service in the army and navy. Over the course of the war, almost a third of St. Luke's hospital staff served in the US Medical Corps. The hospital opened a blood bank in 1942, and by 1945 the hospital was once again laying plans for expansion. Throughout the 1940s, St. Luke's Hospital and the Fargo Clinic mounted a coordinated response to the devastating polio epidemic that was so aggressive that North Dakota's mortality rate from polio was reduced to half the national average.[2]

The second half of the 20TH century produced continued expansion and growth in response to a rapidly evolving medical landscape. Committed to the region, specialists from the Fargo Clinic traveled throughout the state, delivering expertise in fields such as rheumatology, orthopedics, urology, pediatric oncology, pathology, and oral surgery to patients throughout North Dakota.[3]

In 1962, another key component of what would one day become MeritCare was added when The Neuropsychiatric Institute, referred to as TNI, became affiliated with St. Luke's Hospital. TNI had been established in Fargo in 1955 and offered a comprehensive

BUY WAR BONDS

In addition to sending medical staff to assist in the war effort, St. Luke's Hospital invested cash surpluses in war bonds during World War II.

1957

A tornado strikes Fargo, killing 11. St. Luke's Hospital rises to the challenge, even though the storm knocked out its power. To alleviate overwhelming the phone system, the hospital records staff keeps an updated list of patients and distributes it to local TV and radio stations.

1955

The Neuropsychiatric Institute (TNI) is founded, based on an innovative shared clinical model focusing on neurology, neurosurgery, and psychiatry, all under one roof.

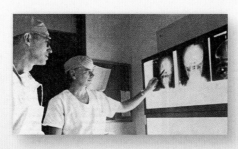

approach to brain and nervous system care by uniting the disciplines of neurology, neurosurgery, and psychiatry under one organization.[4]

Over the next few decades, the three entities grew individually, each reaching substantial milestones and adding additional capabilities. In 1966, TNI developed the first neurological intensive care unit in North Dakota. By 1978, the Fargo Clinic's diagnostic lab grew to be the largest between Minneapolis, Minnesota, and the West Coast. In 1985, St. Luke's Hospital was designated a Level II Trauma Center, launching a LifeFlight team to transport patients via air ambulance. It also added a program to treat patients in their own homes.

Though often working together, the three organizations remained separate entities. In 1986, the Fargo Clinic and St. Luke's Hospital jointly adopted the name MeritCare for marketing purposes, while maintaining independent legal structures.

Launched in 1985, St. Luke's Hospital LifeFlight team enabled crucial health care access to the vast area across North Dakota and western Minnesota that the hospital served.

1964

TNI opens a new facility that includes diagnostic tools and a cobalt therapy unit for treating cancer.

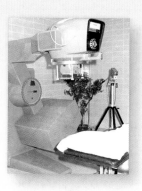

1962

The $2.2 million expansion to St. Luke's Hospital is completed, bringing capacity to 250 beds.

1969

St. Luke's Hospital performs its first open-heart surgery and installs its first echocardiogram. The cardiac program is an important step toward becoming a true regional hospital, serving heart patients throughout North Dakota.

By 1978, the Fargo Clinic's diagnostic lab was the largest between Minneapolis and the West Coast. The Fargo Clinic became the flagship for a system of clinics that served communities throughout North Dakota and adjacent states.

Merging Clinic and Hospital

Despite years of collaboration between St. Luke's Hospital and the Fargo Clinic, combining the two organizations would be a challenge. In 1993, the two organizations, both originally founded by Sand and Tronnes, formally merged operations. Each had grown to be the state's largest entity in its field of expertise. Now with 384 beds, St. Luke's Hospital was the largest hospital in the state, while the Fargo Clinic was the largest multispecialty clinic. The Fargo Clinic organization also operated 25 smaller clinics in communities throughout Eastern North Dakota and Northwestern Minnesota.[5]

1970

The Fargo Clinic's Dr. Robert Story takes treatment to his patients via a single-engine Beechcraft that he pilots himself. Dr. Story made more than 400 trips to rural hospitals throughout the region, where he set up intensive care units and treated patients with heart disease.

1976

The Fargo Clinic begins construction to add another 83,000 square feet, making way for the addition of more internal medicine specialties, and replacing the original structure. The goal is to maintain a balanced roster of internists and surgeons.

Lighting the Way is the definitive history on St. Luke's Hospital and MeritCare, written in 2008 by Carl Thress and Jane Heilmann.

According to *Lighting The Way* by Carl Thress and Jane Heilmann:

> *Dr. Wallace Radtke, president of Fargo Clinic, Ltd., worked through deep feelings with the rest of the Fargo Clinic physicians. "When we were a physician-owned clinic, the culture was different," Dr. Radtke said. Because physicians were owners, they felt more vested. He remembered how Fargo Clinic administrator C. Warner Litten ran the partnership meetings. "At the end of the year he would tell us the capital point and what our salaries would be for the next year. He'd always say, 'Well fellows, we've had a real good year.' Then he'd say 'Wally, close the door.' He'd tell us our numbers and everyone would cheer. We were part of a group."*
>
> *The merger was necessary, Dr. Radke said, to better prepare for the health care needs of the service area. Increased competition, declining reimbursement by government and other third-party payers, increasing costs for hospitals and physicians to deliver quality care, and the influence of health maintenance and similar organizations were all factors. "Yesterday's organization cannot successfully deal with the pressures of today—pressures that will only increase with time."*
>
> *It was important, he said, to understand that neither organization approached the merger because of financial difficulty. The opposite was true. That made it an ideal time to merge.*

1976

St. Luke's Hospital adds a residency program.

1981

TNI adds an $890,000 computerized tomography (CT) machine, with 15 to 20 patient uses per day. The heavy utilization prompts TNI to quickly add a second machine.

1983

The Fargo Clinic's regional growth takes place via the addition of new facilities, such as the Mayville Clinic in Mayville, North Dakota. Fargo Clinic Southwest becomes the organization's first satellite location.

MAYVILLE CLINIC

Also at issue was some overlap in services. As Medicare overhauled the physician payment system in 1992, it created pressure on the Fargo Clinic, staffed by specialists who would rely on primary care referrals. Medicare changes dictated the clinic add a same-day surgery center and a mobile magnetic resonance imaging unit.

It was "a very logical move," said Dr. Mark Paulson, who joined Fargo Clinic in 1988 and now is a member of the board of trustees of Sanford Health.[6] "It got the physicians out of their buy-in and allowed physicians to secure the additional benefits of an employee. At that

Before moving into an administrative role, Dr. Roger Gilbertson was a practicing neuroradiologist at The Neuropsychiatric Institute (TNI) in 1971.

1986

More regional sites for the Fargo Clinic are brought online throughout North Dakota and Minnesota.

1985

St. Luke's Hospital is designated a Level II Trauma Center, the only one between Minneapolis, Minnesota, and Seattle, Washington. Serving such a large area, the hospital adds LifeFlight, an air ambulance service with fixed-wing aircraft and helicopters. The hospital also adds Healthwise Home Care, which offers skilled nursing from registered nurses, and additional care provided by certified nurse's aides at patients' homes.

point we didn't see anything really change, except some combined services like radiology and lab and things like that, but that was really easy."

Having first come to the MeritCare family through TNI in 1971, Gilbertson was appointed CEO of the newly formed MeritCare Health System.[7] One of Gilbertson's first tasks would be helping the University of North Dakota receive accreditation for its internal medicine residency program. "They did not have sufficient teaching for residents, and we decided to integrate some of the teaching with UND faculty and MeritCare," Gilbertson said. "The way we worked that was the person would be hired jointly by the two organizations, and [UND] would have the academic side, and we would have the clinical side. That was very appealing to the people who were recruited."[8]

Rising Waters Lead to Merger Talks

During Gilbertson's tenure at the helm of MeritCare, the system continued to grow and expand. Heartland Health System was acquired in 2002, and a new $55 million heart hospital was opened in 2005. Like Sanford Health, MeritCare Health System had become a regional powerhouse.

In 2009, the paths of Sanford Health and MeritCare would meet when the Red River, which runs through Fargo, flooded, cresting at 40.8 feet. It was the highest mark ever recorded to date.[9]

1986

St. Luke's Hospital purchases TNI, incorporating TNI's considerable neurological capability into St. Luke's offering.

1986

St. Luke's Hospital and the Fargo Clinic jointly adopt the name MeritCare for marketing purposes. Adjacent to the hospital, the clinic is owned by 200 member-physicians and operates 25 smaller clinics in eastern North Dakota and western Minnesota.

MeritCare

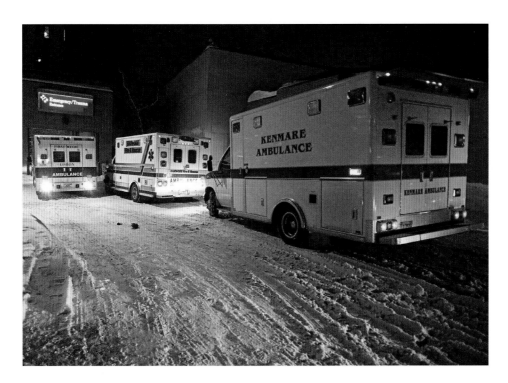

In 2009, the Red River, which runs through Fargo, crested at 40.8 feet, the highest level ever recorded to date. For the first time in its history, MeritCare made the decision to evacuate 180 patients to facilities away from the flood danger, including transferring intensive-care nursery babies to Sanford USD Medical Center in Sioux Falls, South Dakota.

In anticipation of the coming flood, MeritCare had postponed elective surgeries, and by the time of evacuation it had significantly reduced its patient count in the hospital. "The crest was changing, it seemed hourly," said Paul Richard, Sanford Health's chief legal counsel. "It was very difficult to predict. Our obligation to our patients is to assure a safe physical environment, so I don't think our decision was very difficult at that point."[10]

1990

MeritCare Roger Maris Cancer Center opens in Fargo as a tribute to baseball legend Roger Maris, who died of cancer.
The community donates the $5.5 million needed to open the center, which was named after the Fargo native famous for hitting 61 home runs in 1961 — a record that stood for 37 years.

1988

The Fargo Clinic merges with Bemidji Clinic in Minnesota.
The town of Bemidji is also home to an independent hospital that would later join the Sanford Health family.

1990

MeritCare creates an innovative health mall known as Southpointe in the fast-growing southern section of Fargo. The mall includes medical, professional, retail, and service-oriented businesses.

Sanford USD Medical Center admitted some of the MeritCare patients, including some from the neonatal intensive care unit, creating an opportunity for the two respective staffs to become better acquainted.

MeritCare had another significant event occurring at the time. Gilbertson had announced his decision to retire, and the board was immersed in a national search for his replacement.

MeritCare's board of trustees was initially seeking a replacement for CEO Dr. Roger Gilbertson, but was open to exploring the merger with Sanford Health after Gilbertson broached the subject. Still, the board diligently weighed both options for many weeks, reaching consensus that the merger was the best option.

1993

The merger of St. Luke's Hospital and the Fargo Clinic into MeritCare Health System creates Fargo's largest employer with 3,800 personnel. Roger L. Gilbertson, MD, is named president and CEO. Gilbertson first came to MeritCare via TNI.

1994

Alert sonographers first notice the connection between mitral valve damage in young women and the use of the diet drug fen-phen. After investigating the potential link, cardiologist Jack Crary coauthors an important article in the *New England Journal of Medicine*, which eventually leads to the drug being taken off the market.

Kelby Krabbenhoft (left) and Dr. Roger Gilbertson (right) had led remarkably similar health systems just 250 miles apart. When Gilbertson was ready to retire, the two crafted a merger plan that benefited both patients and communities historically served by these organizations.

When Sanford Health CEO Kelby Krabbenhoft called Gilbertson to express appreciation for the confidence that MeritCare had placed in Sanford Health through the assistance rendered during the flood, the conversation continued beyond a simple statement of gratitude.

During the course of that conversation, they concluded that there might be opportunities to talk about other possibilities that might hold promise, recognizing the fact that both organizations were very similar in history and structure, but operating in two independent

1996

MeritCare launches a new walk-in clinic, designed to move minor illnesses and injuries out of the emergency room.

WALK-IN CLINIC

2002

MeritCare announces the purchase of Heartland Health System. The purchase includes Heartland Hospital — renamed MeritCare South University Hospital — several clinics, and approximately 550 new employees.

The Sanford Health–MeritCare merger brought job growth, expanded services, and new economic opportunities to both Fargo and Sioux Falls.

2005

MeritCare Heart Center, the largest building project in the hospital's history, opens. The new center offers high-tech diagnostic tools and the latest in cardiac care facilities.

regions. The growth potential could be quite significant. The conclusion was that it was worthy of investigation, trading isolation for a bigger potential to provide improved access, enhance quality care, and expand, recognizing that health care was increasingly challenging. Larger organizations had a better capacity to handle that.[11]

When the two hospital CEOs landed on the idea of a merger, it was because of the obvious synergy that would be produced by combining forces. "I wasn't looking to merge far off with somebody and have structures or different systems around to create a corporation," Gilbertson said. "I was thinking about having a contiguous delivery system that would expand the population base and would be sufficient to support that level of high sophistication in health care that included education and research. I thought they were critical as the glue that holds these organizations together."[12]

The idea of two premier health care organizations that spoke largely the same language and were already developed, two integrated systems coming together to create something even greater for patients, employees, physicians, and communities, was intriguing and inspiring. Together the two entities would be stronger than either could be apart.

The retiring MeritCare CEO Dr. Roger Gilbertson only considered merging with another organization after he decided that it would be in the best interest of MeritCare and the North Dakota community as a whole.

2010

JULY
The "new" organization unified under one brand identity and one name — Sanford Health — while continuing to honor the legacy of Denny Sanford's gift and vision.

SANFORD™ HEALTH

2009
MeritCare and Sanford Health merge to form Sanford Health—MeritCare, the nation's largest, rural, not-for-profit health care provider, with a presence in 112 communities throughout seven states.

CHAPTER SEVEN

STRONGER TOGETHER

*I think at the core of this organization rest two health care legends that go way back
to the 1890s. They come forward now in a united trust that is demonstrated to each other
through a combined vision and mission to be one of the nation's best health systems.
Patients should be comforted and confident that our great physicians, staff, and institutions await those we serve in both regions among hundreds of communities. We look
forward to serving you and bringing you our best.*

—**Kelby Krabbenhoft**
CEO, Sanford Health
November 2, 2009[1]

SANFORD HEALTH–MERITCARE, COMBINED AS A NEW ORGANIZATION, CRE-
ated a significant resource to serve populations throughout a broad territory of the
Upper Midwest. While the benefits and the cultural similarities of this larger, stronger
organization were clear, those factors were not enough to make the merger a simple proposition.
A plan to accomplish the merger and achieve the benefits would still have to be articulated to,
and understood by, the general management team, medical staff, caregivers, and just as impor-
tantly, the larger community.

The two system headquarters and major medical centers were located 250
miles apart, and their satellite facilities spread out over the vastness of the Dakotas
and rural Minnesota, Iowa, and Nebraska. Moreover, this was not just to be a
merger of two prominent health care groups, but rather the creation of a whole new
entity that would become the nation's largest integrated not-for-profit rural health
care provider.

Both systems shared a common vision centered on the integrated health care delivery
model. Both organizations had been thriving, financially healthy institutions that served as
anchors in their respective communities. The expertise in joining forces gained during the
merger process would serve the new organization well, especially as other like-minded institutions were brought into the growing enterprise.

"I don't think it was just Sanford [Health]," said John Jambois, a member of the
MeritCare board at the time of the merger and later a new Sanford Health trustee. "I don't

Opposite: Both Kelby
Krabbenhoft (left) and
Dr. Roger Gilbertson (right)
had successfully steered
their respective organizations
into becoming thriving
health care systems.

think it was just MeritCare. It was the combination that brought so much credibility to the new organization."[2]

From the outset, the similarities were obvious as both health systems were creating unique answers to the challenges of serving the region's vast rural population. The two organizations also shared common Lutheran and Scandinavian roots.

Each institution also could trace important aspects of its history back to one influential Lutheran minister who left his stamp on both cities. Rev. A. O. Fonkalsrud was among those in attendance when Fargo community leaders gathered above Lars Christianson's drugstore in 1905 to discuss how the community would take care of its poor and infirm. After helping to found what would eventually become MeritCare Health System, he later moved south, serving as administrator of Sioux Valley Hospital.

Both systems were also ahead of their time with regard to integrated health care delivery, each being early adopters of its own health plan, integrated hospital and clinic model, and home health services. They also fostered a culture of compassion and excellence, built upon the Midwest values of hard work and innovation. There were, in fact, stunning similarities in "the way the two organizations grew from their earliest roots and how that growth almost continued in a parallel fashion, and how it was really a natural thing for us to come together and work as one. We were really almost one to begin with," recalled Sanford Health Board of Trustees Secretary Dave Beito, who was on the MeritCare board during merger discussions.[3]

Merger Presents Solutions

As MeritCare's board was in the process of discussing replacement CEO candidates, Dr. Roger Gilbertson's unexpected suggestion that they consider a merger instead of hiring a new CEO left many surprised. Dr. Mark Paulson recalled:

Near right: Dave Beito is the secretary of the Sanford Health board of trustees.

Middle right: Dr. Mark Paulson was a physician with the Fargo Clinic, and then MeritCare. Now he practices with Sanford Health and also serves on the board of trustees.

Far right: Pamela Anderson served on both the MeritCare and Sanford Health boards of trustees.

I was a little bit stunned. I had gone onto the board in January 2009, and in our first meeting we were talking about our CEO retiring, and by our third or fourth meeting we were talking about a merger. Being a novice board member at the time, I guess I was probably a little bit shell-shocked, but then I took a step back, started thinking about it, started listening carefully, analyzing what I could see. I was not too concerned because I thought that the leadership would do the best that they could do for their physicians, staff, and patients, and a merged organization looked to me to be very stabilizing for the organization.[4]

Health care professionals from the two organizations worked together to ensure the highest standards of care were propagated throughout the entire newly merged Sanford Health–MeritCare system through the adoption of best practices.

At all times, the motivator for both organizations was the same: how to offer the best quality of health care to their communities for the long term. As longtime MeritCare Health System board member and former Sanford Health trustee Pamela Anderson recalled, "I was very excited by the great potential. ... We shared a deep commitment to patient care."

MeritCare's board adopted a two-pronged approach, continuing to investigate the possibility of a merger while engaging with recruiters and continuing to conduct a CEO search. "I was on the search committee and brought it up to the search professionals," said Lauris Molbert, a member of the MeritCare board, and now chair of the Sanford Health board. "The search professionals knew of Kelby [Krabbenhoft] and one said, 'Well, that's exactly the kind of person that you have been describing. Kelby is one of the best executives in the country, and he's got the right culture and he's exactly the kind of person that you've been telling us you want to look for.' Here you're talking about Roger's thinking about an opportunity to do something in a merger format. At the same time we're looking for a new CEO and it turns out the CEO of the merged organization would be the very type of person we were looking for."[5]

Krabbenhoft left an impression on the MeritCare board during a meeting that served the purposes of both merger due diligence and job interview for the vacating CEO position. At the meeting, Krabbenhoft presented his vision for the potential of a combined organization and its legacy for the future. He articulated the benefits that could be realized involving improved patient care, research, and education as well as expanded professional opportunities and security for physicians and staff, growth in services, and programs for communities served and regional economic development. Krabbenhoft also identi-

fied expected responsibilities for a newly united organization to impact health care on a national scale. Brent Teiken, a former MeritCare board member and current Sanford Health trustee, said:

> You hear all sorts of descriptors of Kelby: bigger than life and visionary and big ideas and momentum and aggressive and hard-charging. So you have this image in your mind of what this person might be like. I think Kelby has a tremendous ability to be both hard-charging and aggressive, but at the same time come into a meeting and be humble and respectful. You know he always said from the beginning that our philosophy at Sanford Health is, "We don't go where we're not wanted." And that just resonated with me and he still says that today. I think that has been a very key component to the deals that are considered or not considered. There was a humbleness about him but yet there was a very clearly confident man in front of us that said, "This is where we need to go and how I can help get us there." When he left, I think that most of us felt, "that guy is certainly clear about his intention; he's clear about the vision." There's obviously a track record of success there and you know, this is something that we need to seriously consider.[6]

After that meeting, plans to pursue hiring its own CEO "went out the window," said Jambois. "When we did our due diligence and looked at how well we thought Sanford Health was performing—what the administration had done there—we felt the team was really strong."[7]

Similar Backgrounds Unite

The merger between the two Dakota organizations would begin to take Sanford Health to the reach and scope necessary to accomplish more of the strategic vision in place for more than a decade. "We really had a rebirth when these two great organizations came together,

Leaders Define Synergies

Leaders from both organizations gathered in the summer of 2009 to look at high-level opportunities associated with their possible merger and transition to one organization. The key areas they focused on included patients, staff, physicians, information technology, and health plans. These leaders identified the greatest synergies between the two systems, what was shared and what was unique. The goal was to determine the best of each. Discussions also focused on advancing the mission, identifying service gaps, and identifying opportunities for combined initiatives. From these discussions, recommendations regarding priorities and actions were developed and a "Synergies" book was distributed to both boards of trustees for their consideration prior to their final merger vote.

This synergy process involving teams from organizations engaged in potential merger discussions has been subsequently used as a model for determining the benefits to patients in their distinct service areas and abilities to improve health care overall.

and only on the day that we woke up to go sign the papers did we realize it was Statehood Day in the Dakotas," said Krabbenhoft.[8]

"The synergies and history of the two organizations were similar, and the more we got to know each other, the more we realized how much alike we really were," said Jerome Feder, a longtime MeritCare board member and current Sanford Health trustee.[9]

In addition to the regional identity, it also helped that Sanford Health and MeritCare had the same commitment to become integrated and spoke largely the same language in that regard. Both organizations had already developed integrated systems, though "MeritCare ... had probably done that before Sanford Health and felt it brought something to the table there, with expertise," Beito said. Sanford Health, on the other hand, "had this research ability, which was really a wonderful thing to add to our mission and created a lot of excitement and added to our ability to provide health care on a day-to-day basis."[10]

"The Sanford Health–MeritCare merger has been extremely positive from every aspect, from patient services to the leadership to the people development," said Don Morton, a MeritCare board member at the time of the merger and current Sanford Health trustee. "Sanford Health came in with a very bold plan and has executed on that plan, and we've made promises, and promises have been kept. It's a completely different environment today. The community has obviously embraced Sanford Health very much. The ultimate winners are the communities where we have a presence. Those communities win, they win big. Health care in our region is as good as anywhere in the country."[11]

Together, the two entities would be stronger than either could have been apart. Said Sanford Health Trustee

Below left: Don Morton was a MeritCare trustee and is now a Sanford Health trustee.

Below: Jim Entenman has been a Sanford Health board of trustees member since 2006.

Winners Everywhere

In Sioux Falls a new heart hospital was being planned. In Aberdeen, South Dakota, groundbreaking began for a whole new hospital; in Fargo planning commenced on a new—and long overdue—facility.

MeritCare had purchased the land some 10 years earlier. "We've been sitting on that land for a long period of time just looking for an ability to do it," said Dr. Mark Paulson.

The new Fargo hospital is an innovative project, and its design intends to address the future of patient care, quality, and service. "We find ourselves asking the question over and over again: Is what we're designing appropriate from the patient's perspective and from the perspective of providing the best quality care?" said Dennis Millirons, president of Sanford Fargo Medical Center. "There's a body of evidence based around the design of hospital facilities, and we can improve patient safety, improve staff safety, improve quality, and certainly improve patient and staff satisfaction through design."[1]

Jim Entenman, "Through the merger we gained a model for growth that is scalable and has the ability to flex to new opportunities."

Managing the Merger

From the very beginning, the merger process between the two organizations moved forward in an orderly, organized fashion. Meetings were planned in advance and designed to allow the two boards and senior management to develop a comfort level and working trust with one another. It took intense effort but the combined spirit of teamwork fed the energy level as everyone recognized the incredible opportunities to be realized by combining the strengths and traditions of the two organizations.

"Kelby was wise. ... He wanted the best of the best, and I give him credit," said Feder. "He picked the best leadership team and he didn't care whether they were from north or south."[12]

Both organizations were integral pillars of their respective communities, contributing to the wellness, education, health, and economies of their regions. Sharing common missions made the merger not just a good idea, but ensured a smooth and successful execution. "Kelby has a spectacular team," said Larry Toll, a former Sioux Valley Hospitals and Health System trustee. "I've always been amazed at how the organization has smoothly evolved with all those initiatives, along with MeritCare, along with everything else that was going on. That team stepped up. By then, of course, [they] had bought into Kelby's vision, understood the vision, saw it as a shared vision between all of them, and knew how critical their piece of seeing that vision fulfilled really was."[13]

Below: Larry Toll served on the board of Sioux Valley Hospitals and Health System.

Far left: Dennis Millirons is president of Sanford Fargo Medical Center.

Middle left: Mikal Claar served on the Sanford Health board of trustees.

Near left: Paul Richard is the chief legal officer for Sanford Health.

The dialogue between the two boards and leaders developed with the purpose of ensuring that their mutual undertaking would fulfill their fiduciary duties, maintaining stability and continuity of operations, and ensuring that every aspect of the merger would result in net benefits to both communities, the new organization, and especially to patients and their families.

Leadership was key to success, ensuring the continued forward momentum by establishing the proper tone and delegating clear responsibilities to members of top management, and facilitating collaboration between designated members of each board of trustees.

According to Paul Richard, Sanford Health's chief legal officer:

Trust and strength of character were large elements in the merger process. In the manner in which it was conducted, I believe it is a portrait of leadership on the part of Kelby, Roger, and the boards of trustees.

Economies of Scale

Merging Sanford Health and MeritCare reaped tremendous financial rewards almost immediately.

"We've achieved a lot of efficiencies for purchasing, which is surprising to me because both organizations were fairly large to begin with, but this brought us up another level in our ability to negotiate with suppliers," said Dave Beito, member of the board of trustees.[1]

As the organization grew, so too did its purchasing power, an important factor in establishing new partnerships. "With what's happening with the health care delivery system in our country, you're seeing a lot of consolidation," said Mikal Claar, a Sanford board member. "In the interest of trying to

deliver health care more efficiently and more economically, there are economies of scale that come into play with purchasing power."[2]

"Those economies of scale can make a tremendous difference for a smaller hospital," said Paul Hanson, president of Sanford Bemidji, formed when North Country Health Services in Bemidji, Minnesota, joined Sanford Health. "The organization already was in a good position, but certainly the relationship with Sanford Health enhanced it. Even 1 percent in supply expense change is significant in a small rural facility. Anything would benefit the organization with being able to put that money into recruitment and retention of physicians or enhancing existing service lines, and that's what we did."[3]

Integrated Care Grows

Growth to better serve regional health care needs was a key concept for the new system's integrated model. As Gilbertson explained:

> We had a very rich history of doctors who believed in integrated care way back then. I thought, "How can we assure another hundred years of extraordinary advances in medicine in this whole region?" In order to do that, I think that we have to be significantly bigger, because if you're going to advance sophistication in health care delivery, you need higher levels of expertise, and in order to get bigger, you need to encapsulate the larger population base.

The physicians' boards of governors from each organization was used to integrate best practices in delivering medical care and adopting a common set of standards. The merged organization now had 225 clinics and 36 hospitals. A unified plan was vital to ensure continued progress and adherence to the strategic goals. Teamwork was a core value and synergy teams were developed between Fargo and Sioux Falls. These relationship and synergy efforts would provide the mechanism and plan for a smooth start up of the merged organiza-

---

Partnerships and Promises

The prospect of a merger between MeritCare in Fargo and Sanford Health in Sioux Falls brought excitement to both organizations, but in the community of Fargo, it initially brought some concern.

Winning over the community was key. Some critical voices were apprehensive after a previous health system merger had moved executive positions to Arizona. "They saw a

threat that MeritCare would diminish in size and scope," said Dr. Roger Gilbertson, then CEO of MeritCare. "That was the fear."[1]

Executive leaders quickly moved to assuage that fear by vowing that no jobs would be lost due to the merger.

Any lingering concerns were quickly alleviated when the new Sanford Health announced new capital projects in the Fargo area. "That got some attention and convinced people that we were going to invest as a system in the Fargo region … in facilities and … in working with organizations like North Dakota State University and others, that we were going to be an important part of the community, and a very, very good citizen," said Dennis Millirons, who joined Sanford Fargo Medical Center as president soon after the merger. "I think that people saw very quickly that this merger was a good thing. We actually began to grow, which is really important because what we had in this community was pentup demand for services."[2]

Dr. Roger Gilbertson was an early proponent of the integrated health care model.

tions. High-quality health care continued throughout communities served, aided by the best practices and other increased capabilities of the expanded system.

A vast population in the nation's heartland would now receive care from a Sanford Health facility, but Sanford Health's plans are not growth for the sake of growth. "Our vision is to stabilize the health care of the entire region," said Dr. Mark Paulson, a physician and member of the Sanford Health board of trustees. "Now with a large organization, the larger you get, the more able you are going to be to create a service so patients don't have to drive all the way to the cities, all the way to Mayo Clinic."[14]

"That's the hardest part of the job. It makes you yearn for limits," said Kelby Krabbenhoft, Sanford Health CEO. The territory is "a great euphemism and geographic girder that defines our size in our ultimate state. Our behavior as a health system is defined historically by our ability to deliver on what a lot of people have termed over time the 'frontier,' so it's a large swath of country," he said.[15]

In many ways, the geography played to the merger's favor. Lauris Molbert, chair of the Sanford Health board of trustees, explained:

> *It was a merger of adjacent geographies rather than identical geographies. The merger was premised upon the opportunity of having a bigger organization that could offer more scale and then more services, then higher quality services and things that either one of the organizations couldn't do on its own but combined could offer.*[16]

The Sanford Health company bus was a convenient "Work While You Ride" team-building service at the start of the Sanford Health–MeritCare merger, which involved staff travel between Fargo and Sioux Falls. "The Bus," as it was fondly referred to, provided efficient transportation and an opportunity for the new Sanford family to bring about the synergies that had been identified would be achieved with the merger. A special camaraderie was accomplished by its use. Telecommuting, video conferencing, and other logistics were subsequently developed to facilitate communications and working relationships throughout the growing system.

New Name, Familiar Cultures

Immediately after the merger, the two organizations operated under the name Sanford Health–MeritCare and the theme "Stronger Together." From November 2009 to July of the next year, Sanford Health–MeritCare was used system-wide.

Having similar philosophies and business models certainly helped. However, at the core of both organizations was a similar culture, which sped up the union. According to Evan Burkett, Sanford Health's chief human resource officer, "You set a direction, create a vision, and clearly articulate the expectation. [For] people who believe in that, it's not a leap for them to move in the right direction. People are there because they want to make a difference."[17]

Following an eight-month unifying process involving team and system meetings, the vision, mission, and values of the new organization were established, and the new name and wordmark of Sanford Health was adopted.

SANF⊜RD™
HEALTH

Vision, Mission, Values

   VISION: To improve the human condition through exceptional care, innovation, and discovery
MISSION: Dedicated to the work of health and healing
  VALUES: Courage, passion, resolve, advancement, family

Why It Worked

The new Sanford Health is achieving the goals set out for it to improve health care delivery and advance research and education throughout the regions served. Key elements in that success included carrying out the merger to create a new organization joining the two original systems into one. Leadership was immediately established to guide the process that provided clear direction and exemplified key teamwork principles. Similar culture and integrated structures provided a foundation for shared mission, vision, values, and brand. The trustees united in their roles and perspectives across the broadened territory and vision. "Distance was closed" between the various locations throughout the organization with deliberate methods and technology. Benefits of the merger were clearly defined and communicated to all constituencies, and the question "How will this affect me?" was answered for all. Consideration for these founding characteristics is embodied in each discussion and engagement Sanford Health has involving its further opportunities for growth and development.

Solving Differences

Of course, a merger the size of the new Sanford Health system would have its unique challenges along the way. As the new organization combined its operations, the Fargo and Sioux Falls systems had different pension and benefit plans. Every aspect of employee benefits, including employee leave and health insurance, would be analyzed, with a plan for unification developed.

The appeal of growth, not only to Sanford Health but to the people it ultimately will serve, is communicated regularly. There are some fundamentals. "No one will ever be more than 45 minutes away from a point of access to Sanford [Health] in that swath of country. Are we there today? Probably we can't be, but it's the exception, and it's self-inflicted because we keep growing," offered Krabbenhoft as an example.[18]

The leadership culture of the two organizations before the merger had been one of strong individuals advancing bold ideas, keeping true to values, adhering to goals, and continually perpetuating excellence and improvement. That did not change after the merger. In Sioux Falls as well as in Fargo, top executives understood that additional qualities would have to be embraced to ensure that the integration of the two groups would be as seamless as possible. As described by Becky Nelson, an even greater emphasis was placed on listening with a willingness to be influenced, and respect for new and different ideas that might be even better.

Frequent top-leadership meetings reinforced and reintroduced the expectations of staff, physicians, and leadership, and strategies were discussed for ensuring that information flowed throughout the organization. Leaders traveled back and forth along the miles of Interstate 29 to build relationships and understanding that could best be accomplished in person. They recognized "best in business" practices of each other, a process that led to a quick and deep appreciation flowing both north and south for the benefits of the merger.

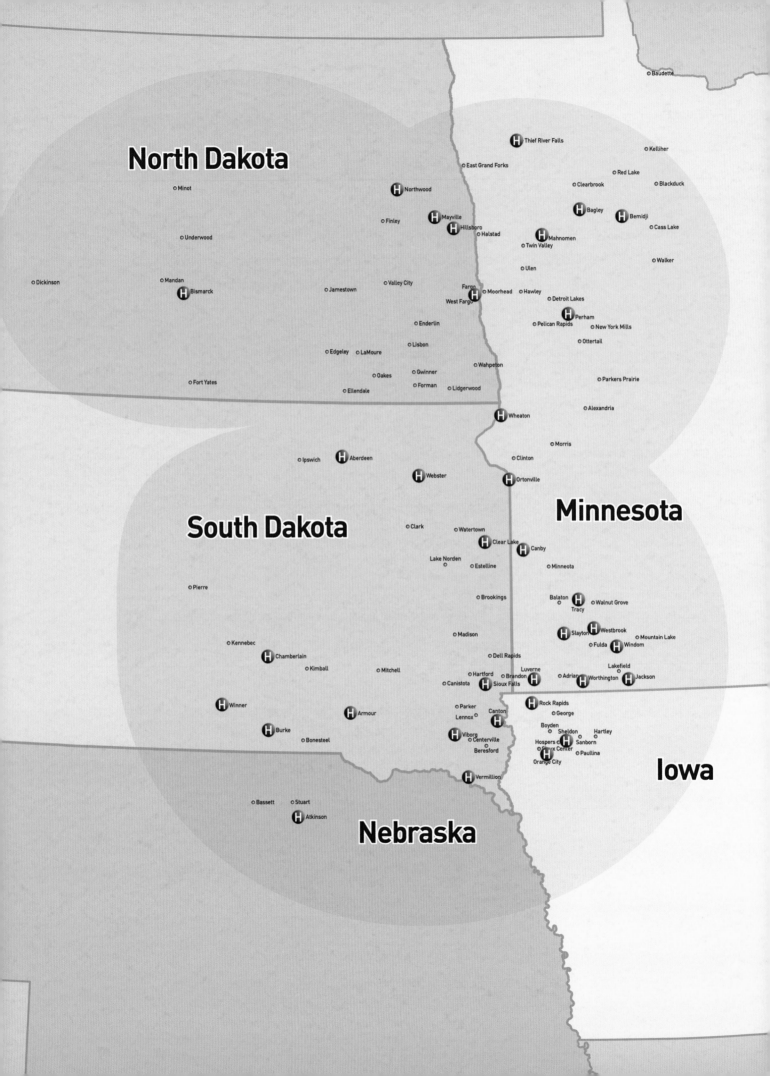

North Dakota

Minot

Underwood

Dickinson

Mandan
ⒽBismarck

Jamestown

Valley City

Finley

Northwood

ⒽMayville
ⒽHillsboro
Halstad

East Grand Forks

ⒽThief River Falls

Kelliher

Clearbrook

Red Lake

Blackduck

ⒽBagley

ⒽBemidji

Cass Lake

ⒽMahnomen
Twin Valley

Ulen

Walker

Enderlin

Lisbon

Edgeley
LaMoure

Oakes

Gwinner

Fort Yates

Ellendale

Forman
Lidgerwood

Wahpeton

Fargo
ⒽⒽMoorhead
West Fargo

Hawley

Detroit Lakes

ⒽPerham

Pelican Rapids
New York Mills

Ottertail

Parkers Prairie

Alexandria

ⒽWheaton

Morris

Ipswich
ⒽAberdeen

ⒽWebster

Clinton

ⒽOrtonville

South Dakota

Minnesota

Clark

Watertown

ⒽClear Lake
ⒽCanby

Lake Norden

Estelline

Minneota

Pierre

Brookings

Balaton
ⒽWalnut Grove
Tracy

Kennebec

Madison

ⒽChamberlain

Kimball

Mitchell

Dell Rapids

ⒽSlayton
ⒽWestbrook
Mountain Lake

Fulda
ⒽWindom

Lakefield

Winner

Hartford
Luverne
ⒽBrandon
ⒽCanistota
ⒽSioux Falls

Adrian
ⒽWorthington
ⒽJackson

ⒽArmour

Parker
Lennox

ⒽBurke

Bonesteel

Canton
Ⓗ

ⒽRock Rapids
George

Boyden
Sheldon
Hartley

Viborg
ⒽCenterville
Beresford

Hospers
ⒽSanborn
ⒽSioux Center
Paullina

Orange City

Iowa

Bassett
Stuart

ⒽVermillion

ⒽAtkinson

Nebraska

CHAPTER EIGHT

GROWTH AND DEVELOPMENT

The people at Sanford Health are united by common roots and shared values that are firmly planted in prairie soil. We are unique in our manner, our speech, our behavior toward one another, our pace, and methods for getting things done. These behaviors and practices are essential to our success as individuals and as an enterprise—and collectively they are worthy of articulation, preservation, and emulation. In order to preserve and extend our unity across a broad geography, over time, and to new members of the family, we bottle our enterprise-wide norms for how we decide, how we work, and how we behave. We call these our rational standards.

—Dr. Bruce Pitts
Sanford Health chief medical officer[1]

Above: Dr. Bruce Pitts, chief medical officer, believes Sanford Health's shared values have helped the organization succeed.

IN THE YEARS SINCE THE GIFT, AND THE MERGER OF SANFORD HEALTH AND MeritCare, the new Sanford Health has picked up speed toward its goal of becoming a national and international influence in health care. It has done so by strengthening health care in the Midwest and Great Plains, adding new members and locations, and forming strategic alliances. However, as Sanford Health sees the benefits that come from growing, it also sees the responsibility that goes along with it.

That means constant communication and openness from leadership, ensuring that Sanford Health's commitment to integrated health is not lost on a single employee, or a single patient. It means availability on the part of every leader and manager. At the community level, it means strategic investments in improving the overall health and wellness of its citizens, not just providing the very best treatment should they become ill.

The leadership teams understand "the importance of the people and that people ultimately determine what your legacy's going to be," said Evan Burkett, chief human resource officer. "It's about the stories they tell to their families, the stories they tell in their communities, the quality of the care that's provided to people who come to our organization for services. The legacy of that team is to provide the stability of employment, the long-term impact on communities, and the opportunities for people who want to be in health care to come and perform at their highest level, and sometimes that means we've just got to get out of the way a little bit."

Opposite: Since Sanford Health and MeritCare merged in 2009, Sanford Health now serves a growing number of communities across five contiguous states.

Prepared for More

Throughout Sanford Health, there is a keen understanding that the health system will never reach its full potential without the right people in place, all aligned with the goals, culture, and mission that exists. To prepare for future expansion, the human resources team began restructuring in 2012 to be able to react quickly and effectively to additional growth.

"With Sioux Falls and Fargo coming together, our focus for the first two years was integration. How do we get people on a common benefits platform, common pay practices, and common policies and procedures? So we structured our leadership with that as the primary driver and it was effective," said Burkett. "For seamless growth, an important emphasis must be placed on being able to immediately incorporate new organizations and staff that come into the Sanford Health family, so that the silos and parochialism that often exist do not, while at the same time recognizing and accommodating local influences and differences."[2]

Despite any differences, however, all Sanford Health employees will have one thing in common: "I want the most productive, best-paid people, and I'll do what I can to make that happen," said CEO Kelby Krabbenhoft.[3]

So far, that approach has been successful, and it has helped raise the quality of health care throughout the region. "Look in terms of the quality of the people that Sanford Health is bringing in, the kind of research they're doing, how that flows throughout the community, and its economic impact," said Larry Toll, Sioux Falls community leader and former board member of Sioux Valley Hospitals and Health System.

According to Jim Entenman, Sanford Health board member:

> *Throughout the system, we have great employees. They're open to feedback from our patients. You know when there's an opportunity out there, the teams lead the way. I think there's a lot of respect for our team members throughout the system, and we've got some great leaders and great managers who are out there in all the different divisions throughout the system. Things are moving smoothly. But I know that's only a result of the quality of the people who we have working for us.*

To be sure, even more health care providers will join the Sanford Health system—no matter how many times Krabbenhoft promises Sanford Health will take a "time-out." "We never take the time-out, but everybody believes emotionally: 'Ah! Thank God. The CEO declared a time-out. Now we can reorder the system, do all the little things we said we were going to do together, because it's been hectic here,'" Krabbenhoft said. "It's always fast-paced, you know, but it gives them an emotional safety zone."[4]

Promises Made, Promises Kept

Immediately after the merger between MeritCare and Sanford Health, the board members of the new organization attended a trustee education retreat and inaugural board meeting from November 11–13, 2009. At that retreat, Ron Moquist, the first chair of the newly formed board composed of members of the previous MeritCare and Sanford Health boards, reminded the members that the merger was the result of talented board members whose courage and vision were needed now more than ever. He admonished the members to keep their "noses in and their hands out," saying that the role of the trustee is to make sure that the enterprise is doing things at a high level, to provide oversight and help with the vision.

The trustees, explained Moquist, have the responsibility to remain loyal fiduciaries: to be informed about the organization and ensure a focus on quality and financial security and to contribute to community development. As a nonprofit rural health system, the trustees have a special duty. "How do you give back in the best way?" challenged Moquist. "And charity care is just one element of that. It's participating in the community and giving back in many ways, whether it is supporting sports teams or other different organizations. Somehow you've got to give back and then some."

During that retreat, Moquist and Kelby Krabbenhoft set the tone for the coming years, laying the foundation and defining the requisite parameters that would ensure the success of Sanford Health–MeritCare post merger and stewardship of The Gift. For any of this to be possible, the cultures of the two merging organizations had to mesh perfectly into one new one—a culture directly descendant from the two parent organizations. Explained Moquist:

> *From day one, we made sure that everyone was treated the same and that we had this feeling of trust and respect. It was interesting because after the first board meeting, I felt really good about it, and I felt that we'd come a long way in just one board meeting. Within several months, a lot of these defensive measures that were put into contracts, [board members] were saying, "You know, maybe we don't need those after all." It gave you the feeling of trust and respect and that it's not just words. It's promises made, promises kept.*

The inaugural chair of the new Sanford Health board of trustees, Ron Moquist has served on the board since 2004.

Krabbenhoft, as the CEO of the newly merged organization, presented a top 10 list of goals. No. 1 on that list was patient care. He stated the need to expand specialty services, programs, and facilities in each region, and in and across specialties, mentioning specifically heart care, cancer treatment, women's health, pediatrics, emergency care,

Above: Sanford Health has remained firmly dedicated to expanding its research capabilities.

Below: In an effort to expand specialty services, programs, and facilities, the Sanford Heart Hospital is constructed, with 750 doctors and staff serving heart patients with state-of-the-art care.

trauma, orthopedics, and sports medicine. He also wanted to expand relationships with regional hospitals and clinics to make sure that the "right care was in the right place," and to strengthen nursing care.

Next was the renewed commitment to research and the Sanford Project to find a cure for type 1 diabetes while expanding research overall. Sanford Health–MeritCare was to launch new graduate medical education initiatives and offer secure, stable employment with opportunities for growth and professional development to employees across the enterprise. For the physicians, a system-wide council of governors would be established to set overall policy and standards supporting best-in-business health care quality at the medical level.

Other equally important goals included the Sanford Health Plan expanding into North Dakota and northwestern Minnesota, Sanford Health–MeritCare playing the largest private-sector role in community economic development and contributing to the quality of life in the communities where it has a presence, achieving better financing and cost-savings associated with its newly increased

size, properly integrating the board and executive leadership structure, and establishing and implementing an overall integrated IT strategy throughout the rapidly growing system.

Above: Sanford Health has expanded across the region, with a new hospital facility in Aberdeen, South Dakota.

Barely half a year later, the Sanford Health–MeritCare board of trustees met on June 24, 2010, and considered the progress that had been made. Those achievements made thus far were significant and all measures indicated that the merger had been successful. The trustees adopted a unified mission, vision, values, and goals for Sanford Health–MeritCare. The new management leadership structure was in place and system-wide marketing and communication planned. The financial performance of the merged organization was exceeding projections, and the regional boards of governors and system council of governors were in place to provide structure for Sanford Clinic physician leadership and decision making. The Sanford Health Plan was expanding into North Dakota and Northwest Minnesota, and ground had already been broken for the heart hospital in Sioux Falls and a new hospital facility in Aberdeen, South Dakota.

The board of trustees approved a strategic plan that had been developed to maximize the value of Sanford Health's integrated health care. This included initiatives to achieve world-class quality and recognition for Sanford Health Centers of Excellence and develop National Practices, to continue to deliver market-leading service and patient satisfaction, and to enhance patient care through research and innovation.

Above: Lauris Molbert serves as chair of the Sanford Health Board of Trustees.

At this point the board of trustees voted to adopt the new brand and wordmark for the organization and change it from Sanford Health–MeritCare to Sanford Health. The unified Sanford Health name and brand were presented at public announcements the next month.

New Responsibilities

From the very foundation of the new Sanford Health, it was apparent that many lives in a vast, mostly rural stretch of the American heartland had been entrusted to its care, and that brought with it tremendous responsibility.

"I remember after the first board meeting, we were celebrating the merger," said Lauris Molbert, then vice chair of the Sanford Health Board of Trustees. "I remember talking to Kelby, [saying] 'this is great and we're celebrating, but we actually now have an obligation because there's so much potential here with the scale and the scope of the new Sanford Health and the opportunity to redefine health care.' The Sanford Health model is somewhat unique. It's not practiced everywhere, and I believe—and I think clearly the leadership believes—that it is the right strategy going forward for efficient, cost-effective, but high-quality health care."[5]

With that strategy in place, Sanford Health now had the ability to grow—and all the challenges and opportunities that came along with it.

Below: Terry Baloun served on the boards of both Sioux Valley Hospitals and Health System and Sanford Health.

Merger Creates Opportunities for Additional Growth

Once Sanford Health and MeritCare began operating as one entity, it could move rapidly, filling gaps in its service areas and health offerings.

A series of key, though more modest, mergers and acquisitions soon followed, including several rural clinics in 2010, based in and around Oakes, North Dakota. The purchase of Southeast Medical Center added an additional 50-square-mile radius of coverage between Fargo and Sioux Falls.[1]

In early 2011, Sanford Health expanded its footprint into Northern Minnesota, merging with North Country Health Services in Bemidji. The hospital portion was a new relationship, but the clinic there had already been a part of MeritCare. Adding the Bemidji facilities allowed Sanford Health to create a regional hub in the state.[2]

Just before merging with Sanford Health, MeritCare had been in

discussions with Union Hospital in Mayville, North Dakota. Union joined the Sanford Health family, and work quickly began on a new clinic facility in the community. The 10,000-square-foot clinic marked Sanford Health's first "green" project since the merger with MeritCare.[3]

From the very beginning of Sanford Health's transformation into an integrated health care system, partnerships had been the focus. "We're not looking for acquisitions," said Terry Baloun, former Sioux Valley Hospitals and Health System and Sanford Health trustee. "We're looking for philosophies. We're looking for marriages. We're looking for partnerships. That was a pretty detailed process. We spent more time on the culture and the fit and the mutual benefit to both parties than we did on the profit and loss statements."[4]

Bemidji Joins Sanford Health

In the months following the Sanford Health and MeritCare merger, discussions began with North Country Health Services in Bemidji, Minnesota, about the potential of a combined organization there. North Country was going through a strategic planning process and establishing a partnership with a larger health system was under evaluation. North Country's hospital and the local MeritCare clinic were not integrated. This had led to duplication and constrained service development over the years. It also created challenging relationship issues between the clinic and the hospital. The opportunity for integration as part of a merger with Sanford to facilitate and advance regional service capabilities development in Bemidji was a key factor in the strategic planning discussions. Through a comprehensive analysis using the synergy team model, the merger decision was reached and North Country became Sanford Health of Northern Minnesota operating as Sanford Bemidji effective March 1, 2011. Since then, new regional specialty services are being developed using the Centers of Excellence format and relationships with other facilities in surrounding communities such as Clearwater Health in Bagley, Minnesota, have been initiated. Sanford Bemidji's growth and development will continue and firmly establish it as Sanford's regional hub in northern Minnesota.

According to Paul Hanson, president of Sanford Bemidji, commenting at the announcement of the initiation of cardiac catheterization services at Sanford Bemidji:

It's what you do together that can set you apart.

Soon after the Sanford Health–MeritCare merger, North Country Health Services merged with Sanford Health.

Below: Paul Hanson, president of Sanford Bemidji.

Moving into Bismarck

As Sanford Health continues to expand regionally, few Midwestern cities offer the unique promise of Bismarck, North Dakota. The oil fields of the western part of the state have created a boomtown atmosphere, with the petroleum industry adding more than 30,000 jobs to the region and $12 billion to the local economy.[6] That has caused a strain on existing infrastructure, including the region's health care. In July 2012, Sanford Health consummated a merger with Bismarck's Medcenter One, an integrated health system consisting of a 228-bed hospital, numerous specialty and primary care clinics, a college of nursing, and long-term care facilities.

As always, "the most compelling thing ... is they're not being acquired. They've been asked to come to the table and help form this system that will now reach the Montana border because of them," said Krabbenhoft.

It is this merger, Krabbenhoft said, that will help Sanford Health "devise and divine what this system will do in terms of its continued reach across a bigger expanse of the country than any other health system."

Sanford Health's long-standing commitment to the community has expanded health care access to thousands of rural patients across the Midwest.

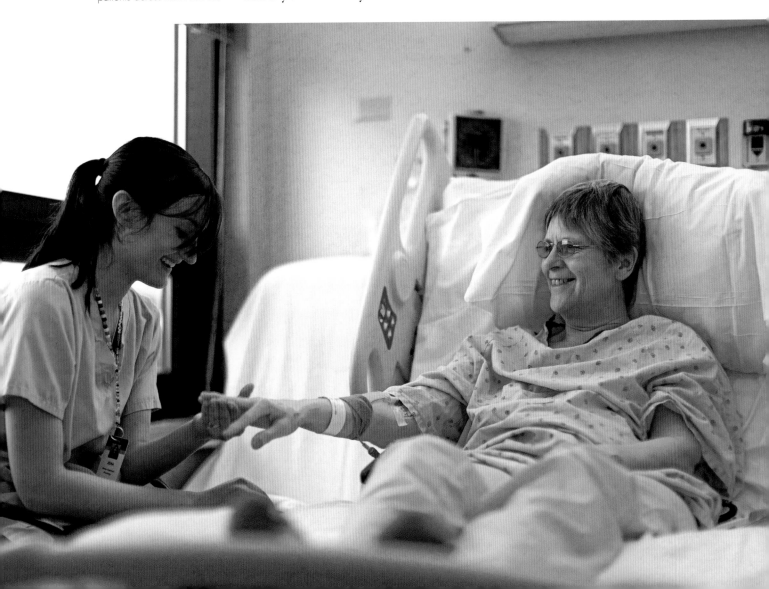

Putting the Patient First

Becky Nelson intended to follow in her father's footsteps and become a pharmacist, but she opted to follow her mother into nursing after her brother experienced a serious injury. Her family roots in medicine include a grandfather and uncle who were both physicians.

Within two years of receiving her nursing degree, she was in nursing management in Aberdeen, South Dakota. After two more years, in 1975 she interviewed at Sioux Valley Hospital.

Since then, Nelson has remained with Sioux Valley Hospital, and now Sanford Health, and has risen through a number of positions of progressive responsibility. Currently, she is the chief operating officer and senior vice president of the Sanford Health system.

"I've always been asked to change leadership roles, and it's sometimes just being in the right place at the right time," Nelson said. "I just always responded to the requests and I was always interested in what they needed to have done. The lofty assessment of my situation was I always felt that I could maybe make a bigger difference if I took the leadership role rather than one patient at a time."[1]

Each leadership position brought more opportunities to make a difference, and each time her skills became more apparent, and even more important. When CEO Kelby Krabbenhoft mentioned to the board that he wanted to promote her to president of the

hospital in 1997, it was soon after she had been promoted to head of nursing, according to Tom Everist, former chair of the Sioux Valley Hospitals and Health System board of trustees. "She had just been there a month or two, and Kelby said, 'No, this is the right person.' And wasn't he right there!"[2]

She was named senior vice president and chief operating officer of Sanford Health in 2007. She was instrumental in building the relationship with Denny Sanford, quickly developing enormous trust and respect, and her fingerprints are on every significant Sanford Health initiative. Because of her background in patient care, her input and ideas have particular resonance when new talent is being vetted and recruited.

She has made a tremendous impression on her colleagues and collaborators, both internally and externally. Rick Giesel, now president of Sanford Health Network Fargo Region, served as board chair of the South Dakota Hospital Association just a year prior to Nelson, and had then moved into the past chair's role. "I got to know Becky pretty well personally working that way," Giesel said. "And we laugh about it now. We never would have guessed we'd work together and I'd be literally working for her. She always brings that clinical part of what we do. Becky always makes sure that we recognize that regardless of what we do, it's all about the patient first."[3]

Above: Dr. Craig Lambrecht is president of Sanford Bismarck.

At the announcement of the merger, Dr. Craig Lambrecht, president of Sanford Bismarck, commented as it being a "big day" for health care in Central and Western North Dakota, "by coming together, we will be better able to meet growing health care needs."

Any new system member will be expected to adapt to Sanford Health's "tight corners," as Krabbenhoft calls them: operations, relationships, community presence, and outstanding care for the injured and infirm. "Those corners are exacting, and that means a certain rigor," Krabbenhoft said. "That means a certain combustibility when we sit around the table and we want to talk about certain things that don't work, that start falling through the cracks. The culture of this organization is very driven about those tight corners. I have found that once people start singing out of that hymnal, they sing well, but if it's sloppy and those corners start getting rounded, then people are off-key; they're singing on the wrong page. Once they embrace the tight corner theory, then it's a function of applying it to what we want to be."[7]

Using Technology to Enhance Health Care Delivery

Sanford Health has come a long way since Dave Link came aboard Sioux Valley Hospital in 1983 to run the information technology (IT) department, a time Link describes as "the beginning of applying computers more broadly in health care."[8] Recognized by *Hospitals & Health Networks* on its list of 100 Most Wired Hospitals,[9] Sanford

Right: My Sanford Chart gives patients instant access to their medical records.

Health has always been at the forefront of leveraging technology to best serve its patients and effectively manage the health care delivery process.

Sanford Health's IT team has been implementing a grand strategy to lay the information technology foundation that will support its health care mission over the coming decades. Sanford Health has moved to electronic medical records across its hospitals and clinics, and is continuing the implementation of the "Sanford One Chart" using the Epic patient information system. Epic is one of the dominant health care information system platforms in the country with approximately 38 percent of patients across the US admitted to hospitals using the Epic system in 2011.[10]

Not only do these upgrades increase the quality of patient care while driving down costs, but they also help Sanford Health to remain compliant with government-mandated privacy regulations. As Sanford Health grows worldwide, it will continue to focus on integrating the data environments between itself and enterprises joining the Sanford Health family to facilitate a seamless transition.

Beyond internal systems, Sanford Health has remained at the forefront of innovative uses of technology to make life easier for patients and keep them more informed and empowered when it comes to their own health care. My Sanford Chart allows patients to view their own medical charts and test results from anywhere they have data access. More features are already under development.

Avenues for Growth

Sanford Health takes its responsibility as a community nonprofit rural integrated health care system very seriously and is extremely familiar with the unique challenges that health care providers in smaller communities face—areas where the ability to fund operations and maintain adequate service levels can be daunting. Consistent with its mission, Sanford Health constantly develops and deploys rural health care solutions through its vast network of regional hospitals, clinics, and long-term care facilities stretching across the Great Plains and Upper Midwest. As a nonprofit community-based system, Sanford Health strongly believes in being invited into a community.

Sanford Health's investment in its network of rural health care facilities has led to continued growth in terms of newer, more modern hospitals and clinics, with more doctors and allied health professionals in the communities, as well as contributions both directly and indirectly to local communities providing greater resources, expertise, and leadership. Examples of this can be seen in the instances of the new projects and growth on the local level as a result of mergers with other organizations, including North Country Health Services in Bemidji; Medcenter One in Bismarck, North Dakota; Orthopedic Associates

Guiding Principles

- All health care is a community asset

- Care should be delivered as close to home as possible

- Access to health care must be provided regionally

- Integrated care delivers the best quality and efficiency

- Community involvement and support are essential to success

- Sanford Health is invited into the communities we serve

in Fargo, North Dakota; Southeast Medical Center in Oakes, North Dakota; Mayville Union Hospital and Clinic in Mayville, North Dakota; and Broadway Clinic in Alexandria, Minnesota.

To this end, Sanford Health has demonstrated its continuing commitment by constantly modernizing and constructing new facilities to ensure that access to the best health care is delivered across every community Sanford Health belongs to. Examples of such projects include Thief River Falls Hospital and Clinic, Bemidji Orthopedics and Sports Medicine, Aberdeen Hospital, Sanford Heart Hospital, Moorhead Clinic, and the new Sanford Fargo Medical Center.

The entire Sanford Health organization abides by the same set of guiding principles, with the same unique values shared throughout every facility, every doctor, and every employee, no matter how far away from Sioux Falls or Fargo. When clinics and hospitals merge with Sanford Health, a defined process takes place using "synergy teams" to identify the opportunities and means for local development and growth. Well-developed standards and procedures are in place to ensure uniform best practices and policies across the entire Sanford Health system, such as Rational Standards, which the System Enterprise Quality Improvement Network supports. Both serve to

An entirely new, modern building is under construction for Thief River Falls Hospital and Clinic, which joined MeritCare in 2007. Smaller community hospitals have benefited from the strength of joining Sanford Health, helping them to deliver better care to their communities.

promote and ensure best practices in patient outcomes and health care delivery and are constantly improved through ongoing review and updating. As Bill Marlette, Sanford Health treasurer, stated:

Key to how we are evaluated is our track record—to execute and do what we say we will do. We have been seen as accomplishing that objective.

With its aspirational goals in mind, Sanford Health continues intensive efforts to improve medicine and health care delivery and achieve the quests associated with The Gift. This includes Sanford Health's consistent focus on all areas of research, development, and education. A Sanford Health Office of Academic Affairs was established to coordinate various initiatives, including new graduate medical education programs such as the new cardiovascular disease fellowship. Sanford Health fosters advocacy in research and education through investing in new initiatives with colleges and universities. According to Dr. Dean Bresciani, president of North Dakota State University, "Sanford Health is catalytic and has already had an impact in our human performance and research areas."

Above: Bill Marlette is the treasurer of Sanford Health.

A True Community Partner

Along with its local management and boards, one of the ways Sanford Health is able to keep connected to the far-flung communities it serves is with stakeholder councils—21 councils consisting of a cross-section of individuals in the south region and 12 similarly constructed councils in the north region, according to Chief of Staff and Vice President of

Below left: Sanford Health partnered with the YMCA of Cass and Clay Counties to build a new facility in Fargo, North Dakota. The Family Wellness Center is conveniently located near the Sanford POWER Center.

Below: Mike Begeman is Sanford Health's chief of staff and vice president of public affairs.

Public Affairs Mike Begeman. The councils meet quarterly. "We felt that it was important to continue that connection to the community, so we developed the consumer council concept, thinking that this would give us an opportunity to be in the community at least four times a year," Begeman said. "We want to share things with them. We bring them under the tent, so to speak, to give them first-hand information. We'll send them quick e-mails about things that might be happening." The information flows the other way as well, with recommendations or requests from the councils to Sanford Health. "When there are needs in the community, we usually get that request ... [and] we might be able to partner with our local facility, whether it be a need at the YMCA or a need at the school."[11] On a local level, Sanford Health has partnered with the YMCA of Cass and Clay Counties to build a family wellness center in Fargo, similar to such an arrangement in Sioux Falls.[12]

Meeting the needs of the community extends beyond ensuring that patients are able to receive superior medical care close to home. It also means investing in preventative measures. A partnership with WebMD, for example, uses Sanford Health experts to provide information about children's health and fitness to a large audience. The "*fit*" platform provides information for children and their parents in four key areas of fitness: nutrition, emotional health, restorative, and physical.

A strong community commitment means that Sanford Health sponsors facilities such as the Sanford Center in Bemidji. The facility is home to community events and athletics.

As Sanford Health becomes larger, it is even more important that investments continue in the local communities, believes Dan Kirby, a former chair of the Sioux Valley Hospital board of trustees and major foundation donor, "It's getting tougher to raise money. I think Sanford Health has realized if you're going to be the beneficiary of generosity, you have to write checks to help things get done in the community."[13]

One of the most ambitious community projects is the Pentagon, a unique multiuse sports facility in Northwest Sioux Falls. The 160,000-square-foot facility includes nine basketball courts—six high school regulation and two professional/college courts, and a "heritage" court consistent with 1950s/1960s decor for teams of all ages. The Pentagon is the crown jewel of the 162-acre Sanford Sports Complex, which will also be home to football, tennis, ice sports, and soccer leagues. The Sanford Fieldhouse includes Sanford Orthopedics & Sports Medicine's POWER program, designed to help athletes of all levels improve performance and prevent injuries, and also will house the National Institute of Athletic Health and Performance.

"Our core business is taking care of the sick, the infirm, the injured, and the chronically ill," Krabbenhoft said at the groundbreaking on May 12, 2012. "We never forget that. That's 99.9 percent of all the financial activity that goes on in our organization right there, but

Above: Sanford Health's innovative 160,000-square-foot facility called the Pentagon includes nine basketball courts, including professional/college/high school regulation courts for teams of all ages, plus a special "heritage court" of vintage basketball decor. The Pentagon is part of the 162-acre Sanford Sports Complex in Sioux Falls. *(Rendering courtesy of JLG Architects.)*

there is still so much that we feel that we can do with the 0.1 percent, and that's what you see here. It complements everything we do, but it is all about the vitality of the human condition, trying to raise up, not the illness, not the injury, not the pain. That's what we do, but what we also want to do is start to emerge the other part of Sanford Health, which is the vitality and the activity; and the wellness side of the equation."[14]

The Pentagon represents a health care innovation that has come from Sanford Health, one that initially began with a questioning board of trustees that learned to trust Krabbenhoft's vision.

"When he brought it to us a couple years ago, we were saying, 'A pentagon?'" said Barbara Stork, former chair of the legacy Sanford Health board. "But all of a sudden you watch it, and you see it evolving. I mean, you see him bringing people into place."[15]

Sanford Health's relationships with multiple educational institutions and programs provide an important resource to develop the next generation of health care professionals.

Right: The National Institute of Athletic Health and Performance will be headquartered in the Sanford Fieldhouse.

In Sioux Falls, for example, Sanford Health has a long tradition of working with students at Augustana College. Nursing students train in Sanford Health hospitals and clinics. Premed students shadow physicians and participate in research.

"Of course, in medical school these days, it's not a question of if you did research as an undergraduate. It's more, 'What kind of research did you do?' So that relationship really benefits our students and their ability to gain acceptance into medical school," said Rob Oliver, president of Augustana College in Sioux Falls. "That's due in large part to this relationship that we have with Sanford Health that encourages research as an undergraduate."[16]

As Sanford Health continues to grow and enter new communities, its citizens quickly realize that, "Boy, it's a great thing," Oliver said. "You welcome the opportunity to have Sanford Health as part of your community because they're really good community citizens. Every community benefits in every way when you have active community investors, and Sanford Health is among the best. This community has changed dramatically in part because of the investments that Sanford Health has made and continues to make in our community. We should be grateful for that, and, I would tell people, 'If you have the opportunity to welcome Sanford Health into your community, you'll be really happy that you did.'"[17]

Rob Oliver is president of Augustana College in Sioux Falls, an academic collaborator with Sanford Health.

CHAPTER NINE

THE FUTURE

It's a remarkable story. ... Kelby cast a big, bold vision and found a partner in Denny Sanford.
... It just really exploded. It's been a wonderful thing to be able to behold. Living here in South
Dakota, we see the number of people who are employed, the number of people who are
touched by the care provided at the facilities across their system, and the new efficacy that they
have with regard to a special need that we're trying to meet with the Sanford gifts. ... It's really
a great story.

—John Thune
US Senator, South Dakota[1]

SANFORD HEALTH HAS ACHIEVED MORE IN THE PAST FIVE YEARS THAN ANY
expert could have predicted. Its continuing mission to improve the human condition has been the driving force that has propelled the company forward,
transforming the region by providing open access to health care while remaining dedicated to curing disease. Today, it is the largest employer in the Dakotas, with more than
25,000 employees overall.

Even as Sanford Health has expanded across the region, it has maintained a strict focus
on improving health care for individuals and the community. North Dakota Governor Jack
Dalrymple has been consistently impressed by the impact Sanford Health has made in his
state since the MeritCare merger. According to Dalrymple:

> *When [Sanford Health] said it wanted to come to North Dakota and merge*
> *with MeritCare, I don't think anybody knew what to think of that. It's been kind*
> *of an education process for me, and I think for everybody in North Dakota, to*
> *discover that [Sanford Health] really is an exceptional provider of health care*
> *and really is on the leading edge of the industry. ... I'm still so impressed that it*
> *can do everything it does and get commendations from everybody that it touches,*
> *whether it's the doctors and the staff, or the patients and their peers. Everyone has*
> *praise for [Sanford Health]. I have not seen that anywhere else in the health care*
> *industry before.*

Opposite: Building on a legacy
stretching back more than a
century, Sanford Health is
poised to reach ever further as
it fulfills its promise to improve
the human condition.

Aspiring to Greatness

By 2012, Sanford Health had become the largest nonprofit rural health care system in the nation and the second largest health insurer in South Dakota, with an expanding insurance role in North Dakota and Minnesota. Research into important medical issues such as breast cancer and type 1 diabetes was making significant progress. Partnerships had been cultivated, which earned national attention. Moreover, Sanford Health was moving onto the global stage rapidly, as its international pediatric and family clinics opened as far away as Ghana.

With Sanford Health's long history of achievement, Sanford Health CEO Kelby Krabbenhoft remains optimistic about what was in store for Sanford Health in the years to come. "So far, it's been a function of throwing those buoys out in the middle of the lake, and swimming to them, realizing that, 'Gee, that wasn't that hard,'" he said. "We've always surpassed expectations. We've always gone past those."

Part of the reason for Sanford Health's astounding success has been the practice of continually setting new goals, raising its standards ever further to ensure a successful future. "I think Sanford Health will be recognized as one of the leading health care

Growing Through a Culture of Trust

The wide open spaces of the Upper Midwest geography meant that when a health care system based in Sioux Falls, South Dakota, and one in Fargo, North Dakota, merged, it was more than two distant cities joining forces. Each organization had multiple facilities in many different rural communities hundreds of miles away from its center of operations. In fact, each entity also served towns in other states, bringing the number of contiguous states Sanford Health would serve to five.

In 2011, when the opportunity for another merger materialized, with Bemidji, Minnesota, the geographic footprint grew again, achieving by the end of 2011 a 130,000-square-mile service area with 36 hospitals, 225 clinics, 39 nursing homes, and other facilities. At this juncture, Sanford Health counted 20,858 employees, 1,010 Sanford Clinic physicians, 396 advanced practice providers, and 200 scientists and research staff.[1]

All the growth—always "appropriate to culture and custom, with the underlying principal of trust"—Kelby Krabbenhoft says, takes place because "we strive to be relevant to those we serve and to those we collaborate with in improving health care delivery."[2]

The leadership team learns with each transaction, as every organization with which Sanford Health merges is different, but "we have a philosophy of doing things one way in general throughout the organization," said Dave Link. "We call those

rational standards. We had done that for years, but we really labeled that over the last couple of years with the new terminology to make it stand out."[3] It keeps everyone at Sanford Health focused and ensures that the culture of excellence is preserved.

Sanford Health has approached growth and executed mergers thoughtfully, emphasizing open communication with its merger partners and the larger community, along with forthright discussion with stakeholders on all sides.

"You hear the horror stories" about mergers that other organizations have enacted," said Evan Burkett, chief human resource officer. "Doing it properly is a lot tougher than doing it the easy way," he said. "It takes a lot of time and attention to make it happen" in the right way, but Sanford Health is committed to that.[4]

The organization takes pride in the fact that it enhances the communities in which it operates, and that some of the biggest cheerleaders are the physicians, staff, and towns that have joined the Sanford Health family in recent years.

In July 2012, the merger with Medcenter One in Bismarck, North Dakota was completed, increasing the number of Sanford Health physicians to 1,200, the number of employees to 25,000, and the number of communities served to 126 across eight states. Sanford Health also announced significant development plans such as expanding and upgrading facilities, expanding air transport, and enhancing trauma capabilities.

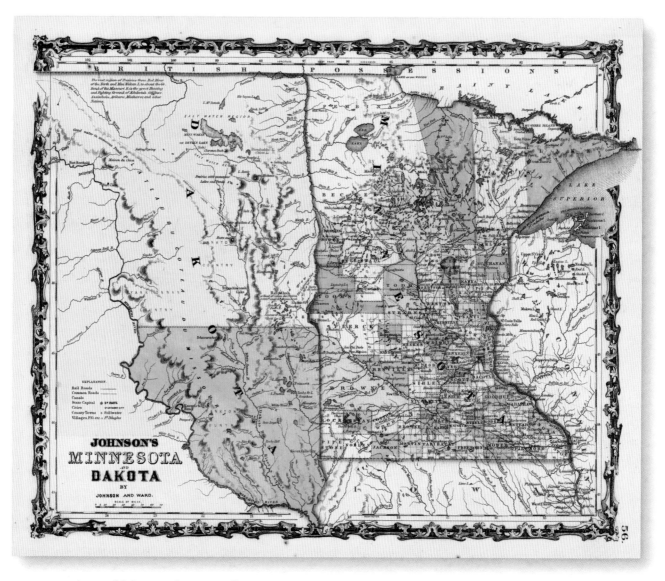

systems in the world, known for its excellent care, its research and innovation, and its global reach," said Dave Link, senior executive vice president. "I think we will be seen as having helped move the whole industry forward over a time that's been very difficult and turbulent."[2]

Sanford Health continues to grow throughout the "Dakota Territory" and beyond.

Ever since the Sanford Health MeritCare merger in 2009, Sanford Health has found synergies in growth that led to 1 + 1 = 3 results. With this new aspirational outlook, focused on goals and a common vision, the entire Sanford Health organization endeavors toward "improving the human condition." Sanford Health realizes that every merger, every initiative, affects the people, the economic development, and the quality of life in each community it touches. Because of this, and empowered by The Gift, Sanford Health is progressing into a health system with a national reputation, recognized for common qualities with other storied systems such as the Mayo Clinic, the Cleveland Clinic, and Johns Hopkins. These aspirations have become the core of the Sanford Health organization, internalized by everyone, and the results are clearly evidenced by the incredible record of accomplishments that is growing at an accelerating pace.

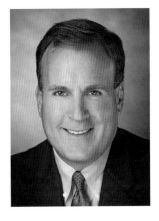

Above: Barry Martin previously
served as treasurer of the
Sanford Health board
of trustees.

Below: Sanford Children's
International Board is a
group of ambassadors who
employ their various circles
of influence toward the
growth of opportunities for
service by Sanford Children's
programs like World Clinics.
The board includes leaders of
industry, media, government,
and an Olympic athlete, all
working to help identify and
promote initiatives that support
"Total Children's Health."

Barry Martin, past treasurer of the Sanford Health board of trustees, believes that Sanford Health's culture has set a new standard for health care. He said:

> We have a large integrated health care network in the US, and I think [Sanford Health] should be, and is being held up as an example of how to provide quality health care. Our performance is being recognized not only from a standpoint of quality of health care, but also from a standpoint of the cost and efficiency of how we provide health care here in the middle of the country. ... We're building what I would call a very sustainable integrated health care system that can be used as an example ... in other parts of the nation, as we move into different economic times and a different health care program with the new legislation that has been passed.
>
> On an international basis, our organization is having, and will have, an impact. There are several different missions within our overall mission that we're trying to accomplish for the future.[3]

With 95 percent of people around the globe in need of basic primary care, Sanford World Clinics embody the organization's dedication to improving health care access. The original idea for Sanford Children's Clinics has evolved to go beyond providing pediatric health care to extending family health care and access to health services to communities worldwide. Representatives from countries including China, Saudi Arabia, and India have made official requests for Sanford Health clinics tailored to their individual needs. Sanford Health's reputation has instilled such confidence that China has appealed for massive clinics,

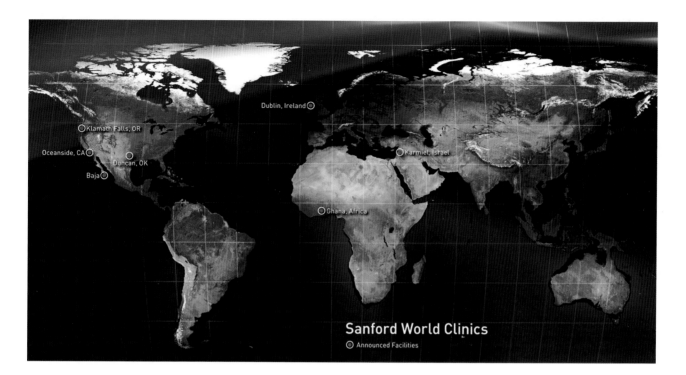

Sanford World Clinics
Announced Facilities

offering to take on the financial responsibility in exchange for Sanford Health's operational expertise. Sanford Health found itself in the summer of 2012 in the enviable position of being able to create innovative global clinics that utilize the latest technologies and best practices by partnering with local organizations and government agencies.[4]

Sanford Health has a presence now on several continents as a result of its World Clinics initiative, and the number of World Clinics will grow in the years ahead.

Sanford Health's commitment to research and development reflects its long-term goals.[5] In 2012, Sanford Health completed enrolling patients for its very first clinical trial as part of its determined effort to find a cure for type 1 diabetes. By focusing on using two existing drugs in a brand-new combination, Sanford Health could eliminate years from the research timeline. "The Sanford Project has great potential to help us keep our promise of a cure," said S. Robert Levine, MD, chair of the Clinical Affairs Working Group, the Juvenile Diabetes Research Foundation, "because it uniquely affords us the opportunity to link in an accountable patient-benefit, results-driven 'cure enterprise'—the critical path resources required to bridge all the gaps in translating scientific advances made at the laboratory bench into new drug and device development breakthroughs, and ultimately, to right patient, right time, every time use at every point of care for the benefit of all people affected by type 1 diabetes."[6]

Other health care organizations have consistently recognized Sanford Health's dedication. According to Victor Campbell, senior vice president at Hospital Corporation of America, the nation's largest for-profit hospital system, "They are a class act, and we love to do things with people we respect and enjoy being with, and the folks there, they really are good folks."

The distinctive culture at Sanford Health is clearly due to "what Kelby calls the 'secret sauce,' that distinguishes Sanford Health from all the others," said Evan Burkett, Sanford Health's chief human resource officer.[7] They may not know every ingredient in that special

Above: A former member of
the Sioux Valley Hospitals
and Health System board,
Barb Everist now serves
as vice chair of Sanford
Health's board.

sauce, he acknowledged, but it does contain huge measures of "taking the high road, being open, and being honest and transparent."

Barb Everist was a member of the Sioux Valley Hospitals and Health System board and currently is vice chair of the new Sanford Health board. She is certain that Sanford Health will not only reach its aspirations, but surpass them:

> *I think we're destined to be the largest, not just rural, but Midwestern health system, and there couldn't be a better scenario than the combination of Denny and Kelby at this point in time, where I think all the pressures of our population, our politics, everything about America, is helping that process go forward.*

Cultivating Top Talent

The strong goals Sanford Health has identified as aspirational qualities include ensuring it has a talented staff. Nourishing Sanford Health's positive philosophy is the responsibility of all employees.[8] "I'm looking at the people that have the responsibility for this organization," said Krabbenhoft. "There is no one else that is going to give us the answers. There's no book that we're going to go to. So it's up to us here. We have the responsibility to do this."

Sanford Health has always been capable of inspiring loyalty from its staff, and ensuring doctors, nurses, researchers, and employees from across every part of the organization are able to maintain a firm balance between work and family life. Sanford Health provides its employees with the flexibility to take time off to care for their family members and encourages employees to focus on their own wellness.

This evolving dynamic has led to national clinical service development opportunities which have helped attract physicians with renowned reputations in their specialties. These service opportunities are coupled with the system's unique research environment and clinician-scientist roles. Sanford Health is creating a broad platform for those wanting to be part of its continued growth in health care innovation and discovery.

This recruitment emphasis has also yielded 135 new physicians joining Sanford Health in 2012, and additional scientists and researchers, attracted by its growth and opportunity.

As Sanford Health continues its search for the best talent in the industry, it also recognizes the importance of advancing and rewarding the achievements of its longtime staff through ongoing training and professional development programs. The company's unique culture includes recognizing and developing leadership among its employees. Sanford Health sponsors academies, training, and other development programs to help create its next generation of leaders.

Below: Cindy Morrison
serves as vice president
of public policy.

The role of nurses at Sanford Health cannot be overstated. Sanford Health declared 2012 the "Year of the Nurse," offering a variety of professional and personal development and recognition opportunities.[9]

Sanford Health is also dedicated to the training and development of nursing and other health profession students, including those of the Sanford School of Medicine and Health Sciences at the University of South Dakota, whose nursing school has grown in direct response to its relationship from a two-year program to a four-year bachelor's degree program with more than 400 nursing majors enrolled. "We now have a health sciences major," said James W. Abbott, president of the University of South Dakota. "Really, without Sanford Health we would have a very tough time

A Vigorous Advocate for Health Care

Sanford Health has proven its expertise on a national level with two laws it helped to enact. In the early 1990s, the federal Stark Law, designed to prevent the conflict of interest that occurs when physicians refer patients to health services they own, took effect. Still, a loophole remained: physicians could still own "whole" hospitals, yet a "hospital" was not defined. As a consequence, physicians started to create and own carve-out hospitals, and focused primarily on the highly profitable surgical cases, leaving the community hospitals to care for the charity, indigent, and less profitable patient populations. "That left community hospitals with all the infrastructure and expense while the physician-owned hospitals rarely had emergency rooms," said Cindy Morrison, vice president of public policy. "And these newcomers not only skimmed the more profitable procedures, they picked the most profitable payer type and took care of very few Medicaid patients."

The community hospitals in South Dakota pushed legislation in an attempt to stop the proliferation of physician-owned hospitals. The legislation passed but fell victim to a gubernatorial veto. It was at this juncture that Kelby Krabbenhoft recognized that community hospitals all over the country could be without legislative protection against the ethical and financial consequences of physicians owning hospitals. "Physician-owned hospitals crop up in states without sufficient laws to prevent such activities," says Victor Campbell, executive vice president of Hospital Corporation of America (HCA), the largest for-profit hospital operator in the country. Barb Everist, who had served in the South Dakota legislature while the issue was under vigorous debate, later joined the Sioux Valley Hospitals and Health System Board of Trustees. "I take a great deal of pride that the board felt compelled to invest Sioux Valley Hospitals and Health System's reputation and resources in protecting community hospitals across the country. We recognized that this issue had to be resolved at the federal level and we needed to be the leaders that went out there [to Washington] and did something about it," said Everist.

Sioux Valley Hospitals and Health System's strategy was to garner the support of community hospitals in affected states, and it did just that with more than a dozen states joining the effort. The rural community hospital operator then teamed up with HCA.

"They were a group that was probably as energetic about this issue as we were, if not more so," said Warren Tardy, who works in HCA's government relations department. "It was a natural alliance for us to get with Cindy and her team. Cindy started a coalition and was really driving the momentum on the issue and we joined forces."

Sioux Valley Hospitals and Health System led the way in convincing Congress to provide an 18-month moratorium on physician-owned hospitals until the issue could be studied further. "Kelby knew that wasn't enough, and that federal studies were often inconclusive and not effective. He said 'what we need is an independent study because we can't prove this without it. Nobody will listen,'" added Morrison.

Studies were conducted, and "lo and behold, the federal and independent findings were across the board in support of our position," Morrison said, indicating that the doctor-owned specialty hospitals were cherry-picking, selecting only the most profitable patients, driving up the cost of care, and performing unnecessary procedures. Eventually, due to the efforts of Sanford Health, HCA, and other organizations and individuals, a ban on physicians profiting from hospitals they owned was included in the Affordable Care Act of 2010. For more than seven years, Sioux Valley Hospitals and Health System, now Sanford Health, has had a national leadership role in the fight to reduce the cost of care and ensure the survival of community-based hospitals.

"We gained national credibility because people said, 'those folks are honest brokers, did their homework, presented a full view of the issue and we were out here for the good of the whole: patients, providers, and the government," Morrison said. "I think they liked that we were tenacious and passionate. Through this issue, we cut our teeth in the policy world, and we now know how to work very effectively in Washington, DC."

Above: Sanford Health is dedicated to supporting all employees, with a special emphasis in 2012 on nursing staff development with the "Year of the Nurse" programs.

expanding health areas and of course that's a great demand in this state and others. We're pleased to have their support."

In charting a course for the future, for Sanford Health a key factor is dedication to research that will improve the lives of patients. "They are not interested in supporting researchers who just come for the sake of doing research," explained Dalrymple. "They're only interested in funding people who are working to find cures."[10]

Even as growth and strategic initiatives propel Sanford Health towards a global footprint, the culture, mission, and philosophy of the organization have remained rock solid. According to Dr. Pat O'Brien, president of Sanford USD Medical Center, "Our story is about what people believe in and depend upon. If it is needed and will positively affect patients we serve, then we get it done."

Below: Dr. Pat O'Brien serves as president of Sanford USD Medical Center.

Looking Back, Looking Forward

Sanford Health created an integrated health care system that is far more than the sum of its parts. When setting its goals, the bar has been set very high, providing a foundation that has continually guided Sanford Health toward a future of success and significance. By seeking to become a prominent health care system with national recognition,

Sanford Health has helped influence the entire health care field, making connections across the globe as it has improved health outcomes for countless patients.

Sanford Health leads in many ways. According to Margaret Schulte, editor of *Frontiers of Health Services Management,* "The story of [Sanford Health] is fascinating. Its understanding of philanthropy as a lesson in leadership is insightful. The Gift didn't happen overnight or out of luck. It came through compelling vision, important core values, and a commitment to action."[11]

The pace of Sanford Health's growth is breathtaking. It has plans for several new facilities, including the Sanford Fargo Medical Center. In July 2012, Dalrymple joined

Award-Winning Care

In recent years, Sanford Health has received numerous accolades and recognitions by many medical peer groups and organizations, media surveys, consumer groups, and even government.

The South Dakota Safety Council presented Sanford Health with the Governor's Safety Award, while the hospital supply chain company VHA presented Sanford Health with the Community Benefit Award.

Medical industry boards and peer groups also recognize Sanford Health's commitment to excellence. For example, The Joint Commission, the accreditation and certification body that audits and inspects more than 19,000 health care organizations in the United States, has cited Sanford Health many times for living up to its exacting quality, safety, and performance standards. The Sanford Medical Center in Bismarck has several accreditations, plus the Magnet Award and advanced certification as a Primary Stroke Center. Sanford HealthCare Accessories has an accredited Home Care program; the Sanford Medical Center Fargo has several accredited programs plus the Medal of Honor for Organ Donation and the Gold Award for Get With The Guidelines–Stroke. The Sanford Medical Center Fargo has also received Advanced Certification as a Primary Stroke Center. The Sanford Pharmacy Broadway, has accredited programs in Ambulatory Care and Home Care.

The Sanford USD Medical Center is also accredited as a Primary Stroke Center and has accreditation as a Hospital, with Certification in Hip Fracture, and Joint Replacement for hip, knee, and shoulder. The Sanford USD Medical Center has also received The Medal of Honor for the American College of Surgeons National Surgical Quality Improvement Program, and the ACS Outstanding Achievement Award as Community Hospital Comprehensive Cancer Program; the American Society for Metabolic and Bariatric Surgery Bariatric Surgery Centers of Excellence designation, the Bronze Medal of Honor for Organ Donation and Transplant Program, and the Magnet Award.

Sanford Health facilities have received from HealthGrades both the Distinguished Hospital Award and the Patient Safety Excellence Award. The American Society of Clinical Oncology gave Sanford Health its Certification for Quality Oncology Practice Initiative. The Sanford Health Plan has been accredited by the National Committee for Quality Assurance. The American College of Radiology has accredited Sanford Health facilities as Breast Imaging Centers of Excellence, and rehabilitation facilities have been accredited by the Commission on Accreditation of Rehabilitation. Sanford Health vascular laboratories have been accredited by the Intersocietal Commission of Vascular Labs.

Blue Cross/Blue Shield awarded Sanford Health with Blue Distinction Awards for spine surgery, hip and knee replacement, and cardiology; and the American Heart Association in conjunction with the American College of Cardiology issued Sanford Health the Award for Cardiac Care, and with the American Stroke Association, the Gold Performance Achievement for Stroke and Heart Attack Care.

Quality ratings Sanford Health has achieved include the Consumer Choice Award–Top Hospital Category from the National Research Council, and the J.D. Power & Associates Recognition for Service Excellence. Sanford Health is cited by SDI Innovations in Health Care as one of the Top 100 Integrated Health Networks.

Media accolades include, from Thomson Reuters, both Top 100 Hospitals and Top 100 Cardiovascular Hospitals, while *U.S. News & World Report* cited Sanford Health in its listing of America's Best Hospitals in Diabetes and Endocrinology. Gallup awarded Sanford Health with its Award for Health Excellence, and *Hospitals & Health Networks* magazine cited Sanford Health as one of the 100 Most Wired Hospitals in the US, noting its modern IT infrastructure and approach.

Sanford Health and Sanford Health employees have repeatedly won various categories of the *Sioux Falls Business Journal* Readers' Choice Awards, in the categories of Best Medical Facility, Best Place To Work, Best Physician, Best CEO, Best Large Company, Best Exercise Facility, Best Marketing Campaign, and Best Nonprofit Organization.

local leaders, community members, and Sanford Health employees in breaking ground on the new facility. The new facility will vastly improve access to health care for thousands in the Fargo region.

Sanford Health is also making great strides in fulfilling the goals of the Edith Sanford Breast Cancer initiative, with research and treatment that also utilizes one of the most comprehensive biobank programs in the country. The Edith Sanford Breast Cancer Foundation is committed to raising up to $100 million each year. Other system projects include the completion of the $75 million heart hospital as part of the Sanford USD Medical Center.

"We have changed the way that, hopefully, people will look at their health organization because of not just providing health care but providing research into breast cancer and into type 1 diabetes and other basic research," said Dave Beito, secretary of the Sanford Health board of trustees. "And we brought that idea, which is kind of a big-city idea, out here to the Plains."[12]

"There is much to be written about Sanford Health for how health care is delivered," said Lauris Molbert. "There is a need for a model that works."

Internationally renowned breast cancer researcher Dr. Brian Leyland-Jones was hired in April 2012 to head up Sanford Health's breast cancer initiatives.

2013

SUMMER–AUTUMN
Researchers working with the Edith Sanford Breast Cancer initiative will have completed first-stage analysis of tissue bank samples from the 175 breast cancer patients participating in this project.

Edith Sanford ™
BREAST CANCER

2013

JUNE
Sanford Health is projected to reach 100,000 participants in its health insurance plan that was launched in April 1998.

2013

JUNE
Results of the first clinical trial conducted for The Sanford Project, involving 54 patients, will be evaluated to establish next steps regarding drugs and drug combinations under investigation to find a cure for type 1 diabetes.

The planned Edith Sanford Breast Cancer Center is a facility that will bring together the latest technologies and the finest researchers in the world to try to find a cure for breast cancer and to improve personalized treatment for each patient.

National recognition continues to grow. "I think people are becoming more aware of just what a significant role Sanford Health is playing in the delivery of health care, not only here in South Dakota and the region, but now across the country and around the world," said South Dakota US Senator John Thune.

Of course, with advances in technology and science, as well as a rapidly evolving political landscape, the future is difficult to predict. Still, no organization is better prepared than Sanford Health to adapt to change. According to Dr. Dan Blue, president of Sanford Clinic:

There's so much change that's going to be happening in health care for multiple

reasons, not only from external forces like from the government and third-party payers

2013–2015

Sanford Health plans to open its World Clinic in Mexico, bringing basic care to thousands of local families.

2013

FALL
The $22 million Sanford "Pentagon" is set to host year-round basketball tournaments, training camps, and other events as part of the 162-acre Sanford Sports Complex. The National Institute of Athletic Health and Performance will be headquartered at the complex. The grounds house the community's junior football fields and other planned sports venues.

and that, but an exciting area is from just where science and technology and the world of medicine is driving things, and the capabilities of what we're going to see happening in medicine in the next five, 10, 15 years, it's like what penicillin was in the 1950s. ... This whole area of genomics, proteomics, molecular medicine, and personalized medicine is going to be just an amazing time in all of our lives to witness. I think we, in the region that we serve, not only have the resources, but the infrastructure, the people, and we can grab hold of these trends and implement them on a broad basis, and whether it's in cancer or wherever, it's going to affect all of medicine. [13]

Through the Sanford PROMISE (Program for the Midwest Initiative in Science Exploration), Sanford Health will continue its efforts to reach children early and get them excited about research in medicine and being part of the medical community.

2014–2015

Sanford Health will open its World Clinic in Karmiel, Israel.

2013–2015

Sanford Health expects to open its World Clinic in West Dublin, Ireland, to serve thousands of families.

Sanford Health continues looking forward, with high expectations and many promises to deliver. Krabbenhoft's visionary leadership, Denny Sanford's transformational philanthropy, the combined efforts of Sanford Health's dedicated staff, and the continued support of the community it serves has led to great success, providing the best possible care to more patients than ever before while continuing to push the boundaries of medical science and technology through its pioneering research efforts. Krabbenhoft has laid out an ambitious vision, one that will guide Sanford Health into the future in pursuit of great accomplishments.

Kelby Krabbenhoft's leadership has made Sanford Health into a thriving global health care system with world-class research. (Photo©www.imagery-photo.com.)

Our intent is to change the course of things. By committing our organization to a grand cause, we believe we can arrive at that place of significance, and you are all witnessing that.

They say there are certain opportunities that come once in a hundred lifetimes.

I suppose those people who heard about those crazy Wright brothers fooling around Kitty Hawk weren't too impressed. No one dreamed we would be flying across the globe in a matter of hours. One thing—fly.

Or how about the day Jonas Salk decided he would begin the long march in an attempt to stop the horrors of polio. That first day didn't gather much of a crowd, I bet. One thing— cure polio.

In the mid-1800s, Florence Nightingale began proving that the sanitary process we use today saved lives; however, she wasn't honored until around the time that Wild Bill Hickok

2017

The Sanford Health Research Enterprise will have reached more than 600 full-time staff and will devote $100 million annually toward unique initiatives designed to cure multiple diseases and maladies.

2016-2017

A new Sanford Health medical center in Fargo, North Dakota, will be designed and constructed to transform health care in that part of Sanford Health's coverage area.

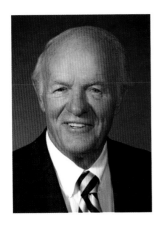

Denny Sanford's magnificent philanthropy transformed the future of Sanford Health for all time and is unparalleled in the health care industry. His legacy is seen throughout the system's accomplishments in "Improving the Human Condition." (Photo © www.imagery-photo.com.)

was shot in Deadwood. Yet around here and on HBO, more attention is given to the gunslinger. One thing—saving lives through cleanliness.

Being the son of a microbiologist, we talked about germs and microbes at the dinner table. I was fascinated by the work of Pasteur and how we take for granted the fresh taste of milk without fear of tuberculosis, because he committed himself in a quiet laboratory to finding the solution. Halt tuberculosis—one thing. ...

You witness today the beginning of a new adventure with an established ship and crew. You witnessed a new identity, requested by us, to focus on the expectations of tomorrow while embracing the past. ... Today, you witness the beginning of improving the human condition, the affirmation of being dedicated to the work of healing and turning hope into reality.

—**Kelby Krabbenhoft**
CEO, Sanford Health
February 3, 2007

2020

Sanford Health will have achieved the goal it began speaking of as early as 2010—serving US families from the Mississippi River to the Rocky Mountains with access to a Sanford Health location within 45 minutes.

2017

The number of Sanford Health international and domestic Sanford Children's Clinics will reach 20. When the organization announced in 2007 plans to build such facilities, it promised five. Interest from around the world has been so intense that within months the organization quadrupled its pledge.

CEO Kelby Krabbenhoft has maintained a consistent vision for Sanford Health, driving the organization to do more to improve the human condition than anyone could have imagined.

THE SANFORD PROJECT
FINDING A CURE FOR TYPE 1 DIABETES
SANFORD

2020–2025

Sanford Health expects to announce it has found a cure for type 1 diabetes, the chronic, devastating malady targeted by The Sanford Project since 2007.

NOTES TO SOURCES

Chapter One

1. Mike Rounds, interview with Jeffrey L. Rodengen, digital recording, 15 June 2012, Write Stuff Enterprises, LLC.
2. Brian Mortenson, interview with Jeffrey L. Rodengen, digital recording, 15 May 2012, Write Stuff Enterprises, LLC.
3. Mortenson interview.
4. Kelby Krabbenhoft, interview with Jeffrey L. Rodengen, digital recording, 15 May 2012, Write Stuff Enterprises, LLC.
5. Krabbenhoft interview.
6. Krabbenhoft interview.
7. Krabbenhoft interview.
8. Krabbenhoft interview.
9. Krabbenhoft interview.
10. Mortenson interview.
11. Mortenson interview.
12. Krabbenhoft interview.
13. Mortenson interview.
14. Mortenson interview.

Chapter One Sidebar:
Making an Impact

1. Denny Sanford, interview with Jeffrey L. Rodengen, digital recording, 4 June 2012, Write Stuff Enterprises, LLC.
2. Sanford interview.

Chapter One Sidebar:
The Impact of The Gift

1. Kelby Krabbenhoft, interview with Jeffrey L. Rodengen, digital recording, 15 May 2012, Write Stuff Enterprises, LLC.
2. Krabbenhoft interview.
3. Kelby Krabbenhoft, "Announcement of The Gift," speech, 3 February 2007, Sanford archives.
4. "Research & Development Opportunities at Sanford Health," PR Newswire website, http://multivu. prnewswire.com/mnr/sanfordhealth/ 33945/docs/33945-RD_Opp_Sanford.pdf/.

Chapter Two

1. Dave Knudson, interview with Jeffrey L. Rodengen, digital recording, 15 May 2012, Write Stuff Enterprises, LLC.
2. Tom Lawrence, "Sanford No Stranger to Giving," The Associated Press State and Local Wire, 3 July 2006.
3. Brian Mortenson, interview with Jeffrey L. Rodengen, digital recording, 17 May, 2012, Write Stuff Enterprises, LLC.
4. Denny Sanford, interview with Jeffrey L. Rodengen, digital recording, 4 June 2012, Write Stuff Enterprises, LLC.
5. Chuck Sanford, interview with Jeffrey L. Rodengen, digital recording, 14 June 2012, Write Stuff Enterprises, LLC.

6. Denny Sanford interview.

7. Denny Sanford interview.

8. "Dying Broke," *Forbes* website, http://www.forbes.com/forbes/2007/1008/232.html/.

9. Denny Sanford interview.

10. Denny Sanford interview.

11. Denny Sanford interview.

12. Denny Sanford interview.

13. "Sanford No Stranger to Giving."

14. "Dying Broke."

15. Denny Sanford interview.

16. Miles Beacom, interview with Jeffrey L. Rodengen, digital recording, 5 June 2012, Write Stuff Enterprises, LLC.

17. Beacom interview.

18. Beacom interview.

19. Maura Lerner, "Billionaire Has Healthy Goal for His Wealth: Saying He Wants to Die Broke, St. Paul Native T. Denny Sanford Is Giving Millions to Midwest Medical Groups," *Star Tribune*, 18 February 2007, Metro Edition, News, page 1B.

20. Kelly Hildebrandt, "$400 Million Benefactor Thrilled With Plans," *Argus-Leader*, 5 February 2007, page 1A.

21. "Dying Broke."

22. Beacom interview.

23. Chuck Sanford interview.

24. Kelby Krabbenhoft, interview with Jeffrey L. Rodengen, digital recording, 15 May 2012, Write Stuff Enterprises, LLC.

25. Denny Sanford interview.

26. Denny Sanford interview.

27. Knudson interview.

28. Mike Rounds, interview with Jeffrey L. Rodengen, digital recording, 15 June 2012, Write Stuff Enterprises, LLC.

29. "Billionaire Has Healthy Goal for His Wealth."

30. "The Philanthropy 50: Americans Who Gave the Most in 2005," *Chronicle of Philanthropy* website, http://philanthropy.com/article/The-Philanthropy-50-Americans/64591/.

31. "Hopes Soar After Record Hospital Gift of $400 Million," 4 February 2007, *New York Times*, Late Edition, Final Section 1, page 25

32. "Billionaire Has Healthy Goal for His Wealth."

33. Mortenson interview.

34. Governor Dennis Daugaard, interview with Jeffrey L. Rodengen, e-mail, 14 August 2012, Write Stuff Enterprises, LLC.

35. "Hopes Soar After Record Hospital Gift of $400 Million."

Chapter Two Sidebar:
Investing in Society's Future

1. Mike Rounds, interview with Jeffrey L. Rodengen, digital recording, 15 June 2012, Write Stuff Enterprises, LLC.

2. "About T. Denny Sanford," Sanford Consortium for Regenerative Medicine website, http://www.sanfordconsortium.org/about-t-denny-sanford.htm/.

3. "About T. Denny Sanford."

4. "New Director Guides Sanford Inspire Program to Prepare Great Teachers," ASU News website, https://asunews.asu.edu/20120606_sanford_director/.

5. "About T. Denny Sanford."

Chapter Three

1. Kelby Krabbenhoft, "Announcement of The Gift," speech, 3 February 2007, Sanford archives.

2. Jon Walker, "Sioux Falls' Go-To Guy," *Argus Leader*, March 25, 2007, page 1A.

3. "Sioux Falls' Go-To Guy."

4. "Kelby K. Krabbenhoft," Sanford Health website, http://south.sanfordhealth.org/archive/Research/TheProject/Biographies/.

5. Kelby Krabbenhoft, interview with Jeffrey L. Rodengen, digital recording, 15 May 2012, Write Stuff Enterprises, LLC.

6. Krabbenhoft interview.

7. Krabbenhoft interview.

8. Krabbenhoft interview.

9. Brian Mortenson, interview with Jeffrey L. Rodengen, digital recording, 15 May 2012, Write Stuff Enterprises, LLC.

10. Barbara Stork, interview with Jeffrey L. Rodengen, digital recording, 17 May 2012, Write Stuff Enterprises, LLC.

11. Jerome Feder, interview with Jeffrey L. Rodengen, digital recording, 12 June 2012, Write Stuff Enterprises, LLC.

12. Rob Oliver, interview with Jeffrey L. Rodengen, digital recording, 12 June 2012, Write Stuff Enterprises, LLC.

13. Thomas Hruby, interview with Jeffrey L. Rodengen, digital recording, 2 July 2012, Write Stuff Enterprises, LLC.

14. Hruby interview.

15. Andy North, interview with Jeffrey L. Rodengen, digital recording, 22 June 2012, Write Stuff Enterprises, LLC.

16. Mark Glissendorf, interview with Jeffrey L. Rodengen, digital recording, 27 June 2012, Write Stuff Enterprises, LLC.

17. Stork interview.

18. Ron Moquist, interview with Jeffrey L. Rodengen, digital recording, 5 June 2012, Write Stuff Enterprises, LLC.

19. John Paulson, interview with Jeffrey L. Rodengen, digital recording, 15 May 2012, Write Stuff Enterprises, LLC.

20. Evan Burkett, interview with Jeffrey L. Rodengen, digital recording, 17 May 2012, Write Stuff Enterprises, LLC.

21. Ed Weiland, interview with Jeffrey L. Rodengen, digital recording, 12 June 2012, Write Stuff Enterprises, LLC.

22. Krabbenhoft interview.

23. Krabbenhoft interview.

24. Rick Giesel, interview with Jeffrey L. Rodengen, digital recording, 12 June 2012, Write Stuff Enterprises, LLC.

25. Denny Sanford, interview with Jeffrey L. Rodengen, digital recording, 4 June 2012, Write Stuff Enterprises, LLC.

26. Krabbenhoft interview.

27. Mortenson interview.

28. Stork interview.

Chapter Three Sidebar: A Visionary Leader

1. John Paulson, e-mail to Write Stuff Enterprises, LLC, 30 July, 2012.

2. Larry Toll, interview with Jeffrey L. Rodengen, digital recording, 12 June 2012, Write Stuff Enterprises, LLC.

3. Dave Link, interview with Jeffrey L. Rodengen, digital recording, 15 May 2012, Write Stuff Enterprises, LLC.

4. Link interview.

5. Toll interview.

6. "SDI Releases 2011 Rating of the 100 Most Highly Integrated Healthcare Networks," PRWeb website, http://www.prweb.com/releases/SDI2011IHN100/01/prweb8083481htm/; Ashok Selvam, "Sizing Up Integration: IHN Executives Cite Common Challenges for Efficient Operations," Modern Healthcare, IMS Health website, http://www.imshealth.com/ims/Global/Content/Corporate/Press%20Room/IMS%20in%20the%20News/Documents/2012_Modern_Healthcare.pdf/.

Chapter Three Sidebar: A Giving Spirit

1. Brian Mortenson, interview with Jeffrey L. Rodengen, digital recording, 15 May 2012, Write Stuff Enterprises, LLC.

2. Mortenson interview.

Chapter Four

1. Kelby Krabbenhoft, "Announcement of The Gift," speech, 3 February 2007, Sanford archives.

2. Dave Link, interview with Jeffrey L. Rodengen, digital recording, 16 May 2012, Write Stuff Enterprises, LLC.

3. Barbara Stork, interview with Jeffrey L. Rodengen, digital recording, 17 May 2012, Write Stuff Enterprises, LLC.

4. Stork interview.

5. Brian Mortenson, interview with Jeffrey L. Rodengen, digital recording, 15 May 2012, Write Stuff Enterprises, LLC.

6. Jamie Ziemer, "Ad Agency Pulls Off Secret Sanford Project," *Argus Leader*, 14 February 2007, Business Journal, page 13A.

7. Peter Harriman, "$400 Million Donation Transforms Sioux Valley to Sanford Health," *Argus Leader* website, http://www.argusleader.com/article/20070203/NEWS/70203002/-400-million-donation-transforms-Sioux-Valley-Sanford-Health/.

8. Maura Lerner, "Billionaire Has Healthy Goal for His Wealth: Saying He Wants to Die Broke, St. Paul Native T. Denny Sanford is Giving Millions to Midwest Medical Groups," *Star Tribune*, 18 February 2007, Metro Edition, News, page 1B.

9. "$400 Million Donation Transforms Sioux Valley to Sanford Health."

10. Ben Shouse, "Can They Find a Cure?" *Argus Leader*, 11 February 2007, page 1A.

11. Mark Glissendorf, interview with Jeffrey L. Rodengen, digital recording, 27 June 2012, Write Stuff Enterprises, LLC.

12. Evan Burkett, interview with Jeffrey L. Rodengen, digital recording, 17 May 2012, Write Stuff Enterprises, LLC.

13. Ben Shouse, "Asthma to Cancer, Targets Abound," *Argus Leader*, 11 February 2007, page 1A.

14. Kelby Krabbenhoft, interview with Jeffrey L. Rodengen, digital recording, 15 May 2012, Write Stuff Enterprises, LLC.

15. The Battelle Group, "The Sanford Project: A Report by the Battelle Technology Partnership Practice on the Identification and Selection of Candidate Ideas for The Sanford Project," June 2008, page 10.

16. The Battelle Group.

17. Krabbenhoft interview.

18. Krabbenhoft interview.

19. "Alex Rabinovitch," Sanford Research website, http://www.sanfordresearch.org/researchcenters/childrenshealth/alexrabinovitch/.

20. Krabbenhoft interview.

21. Krabbenhoft interview.

22. "Edith Sanford Breast Cancer Frequently Asked Questions," Sanford Health website, http://south.sanfordhealth.org/classlibrary/Page/Images/files/ESBCFAQFINAL.pdf/.

23. Jon Walker, "Cancer Fighter Sees Cure Coming," Voices, *Argus Leader*, 23 June 2012.

24. "Edith Sanford Breast Cancer Frequently Asked Questions."

25. "Denny Sanford—A Son's Gift, A Mother's Legacy," World News Network website, http://wn.com/T_Denny_Sanford/.

26. Dr. Eugene Hoyme, interview with Jeffrey L. Rodengen, 16 May 2012, digital recording, Write Stuff Enterprises, LLC.

27. Hoyme interview.

28. Hoyme interview.

29. Link interview.

Chapter Four Sidebar: A Balanced Approach

1. Brian Mortenson, interview with Jeffrey L. Rodengen, digital recording, 15 May 2012, Write Stuff Enterprises, LLC.

2. Mortenson interview.

Chapter Four Sidebar: From Sioux Falls to Worldwide

1. Ruth Kystopelski, interview with Jeffrey L. Rodengen, digital recording, 5 June 2012, Write Stuff Enterprises, LLC.

2. "Sanford Children's Clinics," Sanford Health website, http://www.sanfordhealth.org/Initiatives/WorldClinic/SanfordChildrensClinicsProgramDescription/.

3. Ron Moquist, interview with Jeffrey L. Rodengen, digital recording, 5 June 2012, Write Stuff Enterprises, LLC.

Chapter Four Sidebar: The Importance of a Name

1. Kelby Krabbenhoft, interview with Jeffrey L. Rodengen, digital recording, 15 May 2012, Write Stuff Enterprises, LLC.

Chapter Four Sidebar: From "Computer Pro" to Senior Health Executive

1. Jamie Ziemer, "From Three Different Directions, One Goal," *Argus Leader*, 21 February 2007, Business Journal, page 13A.

2. Dave Link, interview with Jeffrey L. Rodengen, digital recording, 16 May 2012, Write Stuff Enterprises, LLC.

3. Link interview.

Chapter Five

1. Lyle E. Schroeder, interview with Jeffrey L. Rodengen, digital recording, 4 June 2012, Write Stuff Enterprises, LLC.

2. Schroeder interview.

3. Weston Arthur Goodspeed, *The Province and the States*, USGenWeb Archives website, http://files.usgwarchives. net/sd/history/province/statistics.txt/.

4. Narcy Recker, *An Institution of Organized Kindness*, Sioux Valley, 1994, page 168.

5. Dave Link, interview with Jeffrey L. Rodengen, digital recording, 16 May 2012, Write Stuff Enterprises, LLC.

6. Tom Everist, interview with Jeffrey L. Rodengen, digital recording, 4 June 2012, Write Stuff Enterprises, LLC.

7. Link interview.

8. Dan Kirby interview with Jeffrey L. Rodengen, digital recording, 5 June 2012, Write Stuff Enterprises, LLC.

9. Ruth Krystopolski, interview with Jeffrey L. Rodengen, digital recording, 5 June 2012, Write Stuff Enterprises, LLC.

10. Krystopolski interview.

11. Link interview.

12. Krystopolski interview.

13. Link interview.

14. Link interview.

15. Dr. David Thomas, interview with Jeffrey L. Rodengen, digital recording, 16 May 2012, Write Stuff Enterprises, LLC.

16. David Danielson, interview with Jeffrey L. Rodengen, digital recording, 15 May 2012, Write Stuff Enterprises, LLC.

17. Dr. Mike Olson, interview with Jeffrey L. Rodengen, digital recording, 5 June 2012, Write Stuff Enterprises, LLC.

18. Terry Baloun, interview with Jeffrey L. Rodengen, digital recording, 4 June 2012, Write Stuff Enterprises, LLC.

19. Dr. Dan Blue, interview with Jeffrey L. Rodengen, digital recording, 29 May 2012, Write Stuff Enterprises, LLC.

**Chapter Five Sidebar:
New Research Emphasis**

1. Evan Burkett, interview with Jeffrey L. Rodengen, digital recording, 17 May 2012, Write Stuff Enterprises, LLC.

**Chapter Five Sidebar:
Home to Five Centers
of Excellence**

1. Kelby Krabbenhoft, interview with Jeffrey L. Rodengen, digital recording, 15 May 2012, Write Stuff Enterprises, LLC.

Chapter Six

1. *Hearts Set On Fire: 100 Years of Quotes from St. Luke's Hospital, Fargo Clinic & MeritCare Health System*, MeritCare, internal publication.

2. Carl Thress and Jane Heilmann, *Lighting the Way: MeritCare Centennial*, MeritCare: 2008.

3. *Lighting the Way,* page 66.

4. *Lighting the Way*, page 116.

5. Jay Greene, "Merger, Sales on Tap in Fargo, N.D." *Modern Healthcare*, 18 May 1992.

6. Dr. Mark Paulson, interview with Jeffrey L. Rodengen, digital recording, 31 May 2012, Write Stuff Enterprises, LLC.

7. *Lighting the Way*, page 129.

8. Dr. Roger Gilbertson, interview with Jeffrey L. Rodengen, digital recording, 29 May 2012, Write Stuff Enterprises, LLC.

9. Rick Jervis, "Red River Breaks Record Level as Fargo Braces for Flooding," *USA Today* website, http://www.usatoday.com/weather/floods/ 2009-03-27-red-river-floods_N.htm/.

10. Paul Richard, interview with Jeffrey L. Rodengen, digital recording, 17 May 2012, Write Stuff Enterprises, LLC.

11. John Paulson, interview with Jeffrey L. Rodengen, digital recording, 15 & 16 June 2012, Write Stuff Enterprises, LLC.

12. Gilbertson interview.

Chapter Seven

1. Kelby Krabbenhoft, speech, 2 February 2009, Sanford archives.

2. John Jambois, interview with Jeffrey L. Rodengen, digital recording, 29 May 2012, Write Stuff Enterprises, LLC.

3. Dave Beito, interview with Jeffrey L. Rodengen, digital recording, 29 May 2012, Write Stuff Enterprises, LLC.

4. Dr. Mark Paulson, interview with Jeffrey L. Rodengen, digital recording, 15–16 May 2012, Write Stuff Enterprises, LLC.

5. Lauris Molbert, interview with Jeffrey L. Rodengen, digital recording, 30 May 2012, Write Stuff Enterprises, LLC.

6. Brent Teiken, interview with Jeffrey L. Rodengen, digital recording, 7 June 2012, Write Stuff Enterprises, LLC.

7. Jambois interview.

8. Kelby Krabbenhoft, interview with Jeffrey L. Rodengen, digital recording, 15 May 2012, Write Stuff Enterprises, LLC.

9. Jerome Feder, interview with Jeffrey L. Rodengen, digital recording, 7 June 2012, Write Stuff Enterprises, LLC.

10. Beito interview.

11. Don Morton, interview with Jeffrey L. Rodengen, digital recording, 2 July 2012, Write Stuff Enterprises, LLC.

12. Feder interview.

13. Larry Toll, interview with Jeffrey L. Rodengen, digital recording, 12 June 2012, Write Stuff Enterprises, LLC.

14. Dr. Mark Paulson, interview with Jeffrey L. Rodengen, digital recording, 31 May 2012, Write Stuff Enterprises, LLC.

15. Krabbenhoft interview.

16. Molbert interview.

17. Evan Burkett, interview with Jeffrey L. Rodengen, digital recording, 17 May 2012, Write Stuff Enterprises, LLC.

18. Krabbenhoft interview.

Chapter Seven Sidebar:
Winners Everywhere

1. Dennis Millirons, interview with Jeffrey L. Rodengen, digital recording, 16 May 2012, Write Stuff Enterprises, LLC.

Chapter Seven Sidebar:
Economies of Scale

1. Dave Beito, interview with Jeffrey L. Rodengen, digital recording, 29 May 2012, Write Stuff Enterprises, LLC.

2. Mikal Claar, interview with Jeffrey L. Rodengen, digital recording, 5 June 2012, Write Stuff Enterprises, LLC.

3. Paul Hanson, interview with Jeffrey L. Rodengen, digital recording, 14 June 2012, Write Stuff Enterprises, LLC.

Chapter Seven Sidebar:
Partnerships and Promises

1. Dr. Roger Gilberston, interview with Jeffrey L. Rodengen, digital recording, 29 May 2012, Write Stuff Enterprises, LLC.

2. Dennis Millirons, interview with Jeffrey L. Rodengen, digital recording, 16 May 2012, Write Stuff Enterprises, LLC.

Chapter Eight

1. Dr. Bruce Pitts, interview with Jeffrey L. Rodengen, digital recording, 4 June 2012, Write Stuff Enterprises, LLC.

2. Evan Burkett, interview with Jeffrey L. Rodengen, digital recording, 17 May 2012, Write Stuff Enterprises, LLC.

3. Kelby Krabbenhoft, interview with Jeffrey L. Rodengen, digital recording, 15 May 2012, Write Stuff Enterprises, LLC.

4. Krabbenhoft interview.

5. Lauris Molbert, interview with Jeffrey L. Rodengen, digital recording, 30 May 2012, Write Stuff Enterprises, LLC.

6. Ron Ness, "Meeting the Challenges of a Growing Industry," North Dakota Petroleum Council website, http://www.ndoil.org/?id=25&ncid=4&nid=190/.

7. Krabbenhoft interview.

8. Dave Link, interview with Jeffrey L. Rodengen, digital recording, 16 May 2012, Write Stuff Enterprises, LLC.

9. Sanford Health 2011 Annual Report, page 20.

10. Sanford Health 2011 Annual Report, page 31.

11. Mike Begeman, interview with Jeffrey L. Rodengen, digital recording, 16 May 2012, Write Stuff Enterprises, LLC.

12. Sanford Health 2011 Annual Report, page 23.

13. Dan Kirby, interview with Jeffrey L. Rodengen, digital recording, 5 June 2012, Write Stuff Enterprises, LLC.

14. Kelby Krabbenhoft, speech at groundbreaking ceremony, 12 May 2012.

15. Barbara Stork, interview with Jeffrey L. Rodengen, digital recording, 17 May 2012, Write Stuff Enterprises, LLC.

16. Rob Oliver, interview with Jeffrey L. Rodengen, digital recording, 17 May 2012, Write Stuff Enterprises, LLC.

17. Oliver interview.

Chapter Eight Sidebar: Merger Creates Opportunities for Additional Growth

1. Patrick Springer, "Rural Clinics Join Sanford Health-MeritCare," Inforum website, http://www.inforum.com/event/article/id/276238/.

2. "Sanford Health and Bemidji Health Systems Merger Official," Minnesota Public Radio website, http://minnesota.publicradio.org/collections/special/columns/statewide/archive/2011/03/sanford-health-and-bemidji-health-systems-merger-official.shtml/.

3. "Sanford Clinic Mayville Grand Opening Today," Sanford Health press release, 7 October 2010.

4. Terry Baloun, interview with Jeffrey L. Rodengen, digital recording, 14 June 2012, Write Stuff Enterprises, LLC.

Chapter Eight Sidebar: Putting the Patient First

1. Becky Nelson, interview with Jeffrey L. Rodengen, digital recording, 8 June 2012, Write Stuff Enterprises, LLC.

2. Tom Everist, interview with Jeffrey L. Rodengen, digital recording, 4 June 2012, Write Stuff Enterprises, LLC.

3. Rick Giesel, interview with Jeffrey L. Rodengen, digital recording, 12 June 2012, Write Stuff Enterprises, LLC.

Chapter Nine

1. John Thune, interview with Jeffrey L. Rodengen, digital recording, 2 July 2012, Write Stuff Enterprises, LLC.

2. Dave Link, interview with Jeffrey L. Rodengen, digital recording, 16 May 2012, Write Stuff Enterprises, LLC.

3. Barry Martin, interview with Jeffrey L. Rodengen, digital recording, 29 June 2012, Write Stuff Enterprises, LLC.

4. Link interview.

5. *Sharing the Dream—From Success to Significance,* unpublished manuscript, Sanford Health archives.

6. "Reactions/Quotes," Sanford Health website, http://south.sanfordhealth.org/archive/Research/TheProject/ReactionsQuotes/.

7. Evan Burkett, interview with Jeffrey L. Rodengen, digital recording, 17 May 2012, Write Stuff Enterprises, LLC.

8. Link interview.

9. Kelby Krabbenhoft, interview with Jeffrey L. Rodengen, digital recording, 15 May 2012, Write Stuff Enterprises, LLC.

10. Jack Dalrymple, interview with Jeffrey L. Rodengen, digital recording, 1 August 2012, Write Stuff Enterprises LLC.

11. Margaret Schulte, editorial in reference to "Philanthropy: A Priceless Lesson in Healthcare Leadership—The Sanford Health Story," *Frontiers in Health Management,* Summer 2008, volume 24, issue 4.

12. Dave Beito, interview with Jeffrey L. Rodengen, digital recording, 29 May 2012, Write Stuff Enterprises, LLC.

13. Dr. Dan Blue, interview with Jeffrey L. Rodengen, digital recording, 29 May 2012, Write Stuff Enterprises, LLC.

Chapter Nine Sidebar:
Growing Through a Culture of Trust

1. Sanford Health 2011 Annual Report.

2. Sanford Health 2011 Annual Report.

3. Dave Link, interview with Jeffrey L. Rodengen, digital recording, 16 May 2012, Write Stuff Enterprises, LLC.

4. Evan Burkett, interview with Jeffrey L. Rodengen, digital recording, 17 May 2012, Write Stuff Enterprises, LLC.

INDEX

Page numbers in **bold italics** indicate photographs.

The Heritage of Sanford Health

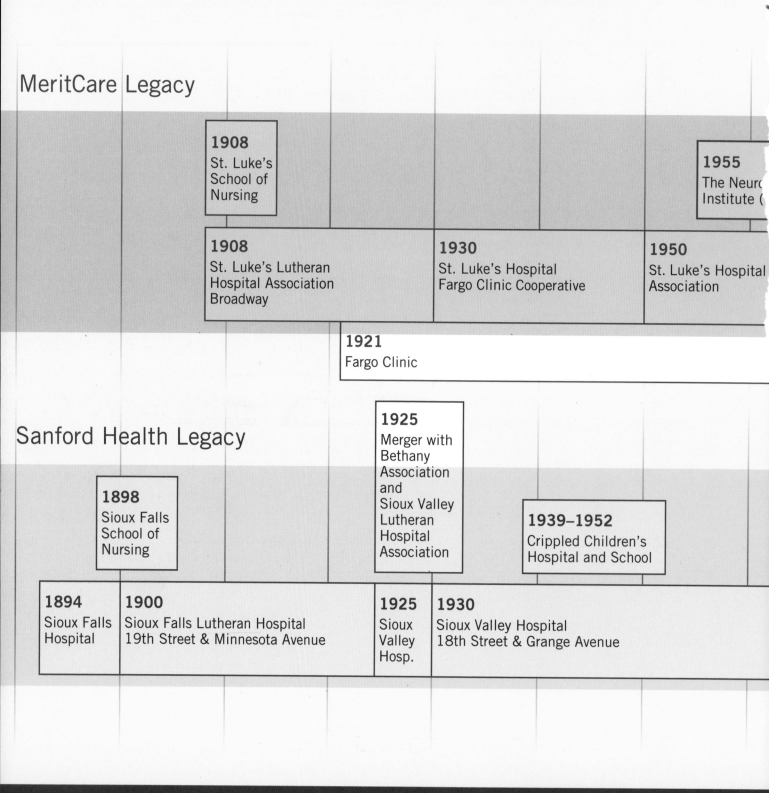

MeritCare Legacy

1908
St. Luke's
School of
Nursing

1955
The Neuro
Institute (

1908
St. Luke's Lutheran
Hospital Association
Broadway

1930
St. Luke's Hospital
Fargo Clinic Cooperative

1950
St. Luke's Hospital
Association

1921
Fargo Clinic

Sanford Health Legacy

1925
Merger with
Bethany
Association
and
Sioux Valley
Lutheran
Hospital
Association

1939–1952
Crippled Children's
Hospital and School

1898
Sioux Falls
School of
Nursing

1894
Sioux Falls
Hospital

1900
Sioux Falls Lutheran Hospital
19th Street & Minnesota Avenue

1925
Sioux
Valley
Hosp.

1930
Sioux Valley Hospital
18th Street & Grange Avenue

| 1890 | 1900 | 1910 | 1920 | 1930 | 1940 | 1950 |